THE M

GW00995101

'. . . when you have eli[m]
remains, *however improbable*, must be the truth.'

Sherlock Holmes

You are a private detective – one of the best. You are summoned by a top man at Scotland Yard to solve a crime which at first glance has no motive and which for security reasons has to be handled with kid gloves. Only you can help.

You are T.S., the troubleshooter – ace crime-solver, last resort of the police and security forces. You need to be tough, determined, but above all cool, smart and nobody's fool.

A policeman was warned about the bomb at the Bank of England. There was plenty of time to defuse it. No harm was caused and no one claimed responsibility. Initial investigations reveal an international web of intrigue which only a professional can attempt to unravel.

THE MONEY SPIDER is part game, part book, and your role as T.S. is not only to solve the crime, but to prove it!

The rules are simple – all you need are this book, a pencil, an eraser and the mind of a smart detective.

Scotland Yard expect results quickly, while the criminals are using every minute to cover up their tracks. Action is needed!

Robin Waterfield was a university lecturer in Classics and is now a self-employed writer and editor. His books include *Plato: Philebus* and *Plato: Theaetetus*, which are Penguin Classics, and *Rebel Planet*, *Masks of Mayhem* and *Phantoms of Fear*, which are Puffin Fighting Fantasy Gamebooks. Wilfred Davies has had many different jobs including ten years in the RAF, bookseller, diesel mechanic, jeweller, accountant, writer and translator! They met in Manchester in 1973, both now live in London, both are married and both have two children.

THE MONEY SPIDER

Robin Waterfield and Wilfred Davies

Illustrated by Malcolm Barter

PENGUIN BOOKS

PENGUIN BOOKS

Published by the Penguin Group
27 Wrights Lane, London w8 5tz, England
Viking Penguin Inc., 40 West 23rd Street, New York, New York 10010, USA
Penguin Books Australia Ltd, Ringwood, Victoria, Australia
Penguin Books Canada Ltd, 2801 John Street, Markham, Ontario, Canada l3r 1b4
Penguin Books (NZ) Ltd, 182–190 Wairau Road, Auckland 10, New Zealand

Penguin Books Ltd, Registered Offices: Harmondsworth, Middlesex, England

First published 1988

Made and printed in Great Britain by
Cox and Wyman Ltd, Reading, Berks
Filmset in 11/13 Linotron Palatino by
Rowland Phototypesetting Ltd,
Bury St Edmunds, Suffolk

To T.D. and E.D.

CONTENTS

INTRODUCTION

9

HOW TO SOLVE THE CRIME

10

THE WEB

13

HINTS ON PLAY

15

File

16

The Web

17

THE MONEY SPIDER

19

INTRODUCTION

You are a private detective. Because you have been very successful in solving the crimes you have tackled in the past, you have valuable contacts among the British police, Interpol, and many of the police and security forces of friendly nations. Among the crimes you have dealt with are complicated and delicate ones, such as kidnappings or the recovery of insured jewels, and even the security forces have been known to seek your help. In this way you have amassed a considerable personal fortune, the respect of the authorities – and even grudging admiration from criminals.

They call you the troubleshooter, the one who sorts out the difficult problems. You are T.S. In many cases, you are the only hope for police forces, or for individuals in trouble. When your phone rings on your unlisted number, you must be ready. And there it goes – it could be anything!

How to Solve the Crime

This book is a game as well as a story. You might succeed in solving the crime; you might solve it, but be unable to prove it; or you might fail to solve it at all! The rules are simple: you need the book, a pencil, an eraser – and, of course, your intelligence.

Luck and intuition play some part in detective work: after all, sometimes there is little to tell between a false trail and a true one! As an experienced detective, you know that when you dig into people's lives something odd or even suspicious often emerges. So intuition and your natural flair as a detective can help you to decide which matters are relevant to your case and which are not; but intelligence is a better tool and should be used wherever possible. Don't guess; don't rush blindly ahead – think! You might even be able to work it out!

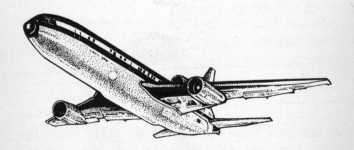

The world of the detective is not ideal. As a private detective, you are independent of organizations: you need consult no one and nothing except your own best interests before deciding to fly off to Timbuktu. But since you are employed by organizations, they can also pull you off the case. You might be taking too long, for too few results; you could be stirring up political troubles, or have irritated some powerful person who can pull strings against you; you may even have acted illegally and been caught at it!

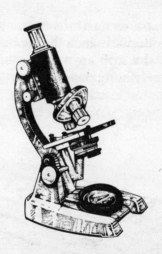

Be thorough, but also be economical. If you are economical, your clients will not worry about the cost of your services. If you are thorough, you will get the evidence you need to convict the villains. A combination of economy, intelligence, flair and thoroughness is what you need.

Your past successes, especially with 'unsolvable' cases, have been based on your application of traditional methods and your own flair. The three traditional factors are motive, means and opportunity.

All crimes have some reason for being committed: this is motive. The crime was carried out in some way: this is the means. All crimes must involve a time when the criminal and the victim coincide and circumstances favourable for the meeting: this is the opportunity.

For instance, someone has been hit on the head and robbed. The motive is gain; the means is some blunt instrument; the opportunity is some dark alley away from interfering police or curious passers-by.

No investigation is absolutely complete until the motive, the means and the opportunity have all been discovered and proved. This is thoroughness; this is professional. And you are good at it – that's why you are T.S., the troubleshooter.

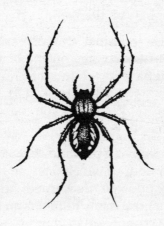

The Web

Page 16 of the book has been left blank for you to jot down any notes that you want about the case: treat it as a file or dossier about the crime and your suspects. Opposite this blank page is a diagram – a spider's web, in which the segments of the Web contain numbers, from 1 to 72.

During the course of the book, whenever some avenue of investigation has been completed, or some significant factor emerges, the book will tell you to mark a certain number on the Web. This number will be random: you cannot chart the course of your investigation by following a sequence of numbers. Use your pencil lightly to mark on the Web whatever numbers the book tells you to mark. *If* you are going to play the book as a game, it is essential that you follow the instructions about marking numbers on the Web.

You may like to match this process of marking numbers with your notes on the blank page. For instance, you have just found the blunt instrument used in a mugging. The book tells you to mark number 1 on the Web, and you make a note: '1 – blunt instrument'.

No detective knows in advance how many clues he or she has to find, or which ones, in order to solve the crime. Nor do you. Be warned, however: if you are marking a great many numbers on the Web, you are not being economical in your investigation.

Hints on Play

To summarize: look before you leap; and be thorough, but economical.

It will be obvious as soon as you begin to read the book that the paragraphs make no sense if they are read in order. At the end of each paragraph or section, you will be directed to further sections. Do as the book says, otherwise it'll be no fun! In some situations, you will be faced with a number of choices; at other times, you will have committed yourself to a course of action, and the book will offer you fewer choices.

There is one optimum route towards a successful conclusion, but there are many other routes! You may not succeed the first time you play the game, but what you learned then will be of use in your next attempts, as you create for yourself another series of adventures, another story.

You can now begin your investigation. Good luck, T.S. Remember Sherlock Holmes's maxim: '. . . when you have eliminated the impossible, whatever remains, *however improbable*, must be the truth.' You'd better begin by answering the phone, which has been ringing ever since page 9! Turn to paragraph 1.

File

English teenager

48 cheese ✓
42 explosive ✓
32 klaus ✓
10 dock
8 Pippin
2 teenager

The Web

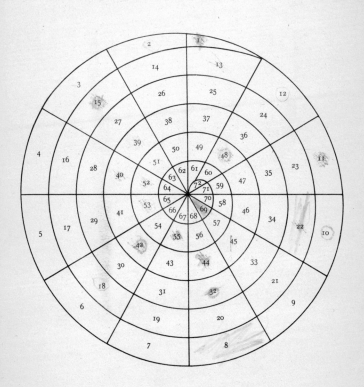

1

At the other end of the phone is Chief Superintendent Boyson of Scotland Yard. A former military man, he does not beat about the bush: 'T.S., we need you. There's been a bomb at the Bank of England. Some peculiar features to the case.'

You go straight down and gain entry to the cordoned-off area of Threadneedle Street in the City of London, and before long you have learned what there is to learn about this event. It certainly does not appear to be a straightforward case.

At 9.20 a.m. an English teenager informed a police constable on his beat that there was a bomb at the Bank of England. The constable, fearing terrorist activity, raced off to Threadneedle Street, where the teenager melted into the crowds thronging the district. By 9.30 the area had been cordoned off, and the building and nearby offices had been evacuated.

By 9.38 the bomb was safe. What the Bomb Squad found was this: a fairly simple, and not particularly powerful bomb, consisting of plastic explosive, had been placed, in a thick brown-paper bag, in one of the alcoves containing statues at the front of the Bank. There was a timer, due to trigger the bomb at 10.10 exactly; but, most peculiarly, there was also an alarm clock in the bag, which was not connected to the bomb, and was due to go off at 9.50.

No fingerprints appear on the relevant items except those of members of the Bomb Squad, and you search around in vain for any other clues. This is all you have to go on. There is nothing more you can do at the scene of the crime, so you return to your office. Within a few hours, the preliminary report on the incident is on your desk. The police are meanwhile collating all further data which could be relevant. Turn to **100**.

2

There is a report of a robbery having taken place at 9.35 in the Hatton Garden district. A wholesale jeweller was robbed of gold rings and chains worth about £100,000. The wholesalers is situated on Cowcross Street and the thieves drove away through Smithfield Market and down Little Britain. The car was later found abandoned in Fore Street, near Moorgate Station. The thieves had expert knowledge of the goods: they took only the choice items. The method used suggests that a particular team of villains, who are known to the police, was involved. The police keep records of the methods used in crimes (a method is known as a *modus operandi*, or MO for short) and it is not difficult for them to link one crime to another because of their MOs. This particular gang has been known to use explosives for safe-cracking, but as far as the police know they have never previously planted a bomb in a public place. However, they have the expertise, and they are a pretty heavy mob. Turn to **77**.

3

The next day, you pay another visit to the bank, and this time they co-operate. You hear a fascinating story. The account has a standing amount in it of $100,000; and, as this is drawn on, more is paid in to keep the account at that level. There are ten different people who pay into this account, and they do so in strict rotation. The bank pays all the bills; the only restriction is that Spinne always has to quote his personal number. There has never been any problem, except once when the next person on the list died, but he was soon replaced by someone else.

Your next step is to try to find out who these people are who are willing to pay a Swiss shoemaker's bills, no matter how high. Is it blackmail? What do they all have in common? They come from all over the world: there is one South African, one American, one German, one Englishman, two from France, two Israelis and two Italians.

You look for common denominators. Four of them, the oldest ones, have something in common: during the Second World War, they all escaped from Nazi Germany via Switzerland. Two of them are women. Only one of them, an Italian, has any known criminal connections. The only common thread is that they are all extremely rich. However persistent your discreet inquiries, you can uncover nothing suspicious. Turn to **50**.

4

The next day you go to the night club. The manager
gets out the membership list and you also question
the doorman, who remembers the party very well.
Charles Trencham, the member who was talking
about the banker, has an address in Hampstead and
you take a taxi to his home. You have to wait until
the evening for him to arrive home; then you question him. At first he is reluctant to talk; it seems that
he gossips only when he is drunk! But when you
press him, he says, 'Well, y'know, it was quite a
surprise. I'd been working late and was on my
way to the station, and there was one of those
cleaning thingummies. It stopped and a team of
four of them toddled out, sort of brooms and
bazookas at the ready. Well, I'll swear that one
of them was Lisa Goch. Well, meantersay, she's
a banker, what? High flier too; Swiss, I think.
Works for Hessemann and Pinelli, respected private
bank and all that. Why should she be in cleaner's
uniform – moonlighting or something?' You ask
what day he is talking about: it is the evening
of the day of the bomb. You ask what cleaning
company. It comes back to him in a moment:
Intercon. Turn to **85**.

5

The tutor returns and says that the Eagle will be in
the gardens of Magdalene College at three o'clock.
You go there at the appointed time. The Eagle looks
at you, summing you up. Then he says, 'So you're
T. S.' There is scorn in his voice. He continues: 'Take

the Trumpington Road and walk for half a mile. Walk, do not drive. I'll see you there.'

As you walk along the road, you realize why he has made these arrangements: the stretch you are on is straight and you can be seen for some distance. His car draws up beside you and he tells you to sit in the back. He drives two hundred yards, and then he tells you to sit in the front. He says, 'Well, you appear not to have any electronic devices on you or any weapons; nor were you accompanied along the road. We'll go and have a drink together.' He must have rigged up some sort of electronic detection device in the back of the car.

You pull up at a pub called the Volunteer and sit outside. He seems to be a nice enough person – until you remember what he has done. You ask him straight out whether he knows anything about the Bank bomb scare. He shakes his head. 'No,' he says. 'I can state without error that it was not a politically sensitive act.' That means that his contacts were not involved either. You get into the car and return to Cambridge. Turn to **213**.

6

Back in London you review what you have got: a number of suspicions, but little or no hard proof, it seems. You are fed up with the whole case; you can see no profit in it. You confide your suspicions to the police and take yourself off the case. Your lack of persistence will not make you popular among those who may require your services in the future.

7

You find that one of the two Swiss entrants listed as entering the country with a tour party can be eliminated: he is too tall and thin to match Cohen's description. The other did not stay with the tour and should therefore have been listed as a 'Single Visitor'. This is not necessarily suspicious: it is quite a common trick, simply to save money, to get on to a cheap package tour to some country, but then leave the tour once you are in the country. Nevertheless, you check up on this person, Wolf Spinne, from the canton of Untersee in Switzerland.

You go to his hotel and examine the details of his passport, what phone calls he made, meals he ate, messages received, visitors to his room, and so on. But you find nothing to make him a suspicious character. His passport gives his age as fifty-nine and states that he has a limp, so at any rate he cannot be the one who told Cohen to tell the policeman about the bomb: Cohen would have mentioned a limp. The one oddity is that, although his passport declares his profession to be shoemaker, the hotel he stayed at is expensive and he seems not to have spared expense in the meals he ate either. Mark 39 on the Web. If you want to check up on more Swiss visitors, turn to **73** and choose again. If you want to check up on German visitors, turn to **163**, or you may still need to investigate the Austrian visitors (turn to **60**). If you have finished looking into the visitors, turn to **200**.

8

There is really no need to carry on now, since you have plenty of time to get into position by dusk tomorrow. The half-light makes appearances deceptive. You are stepping from one rock to another, but fail to see a projecting ledge. You fall awkwardly and break your ankle. You can crawl to shelter, although this is agony, and make yourself warm for the night, but in the morning it is all you can do to call for help until another climber arrives. You have lost the element of surprise and have no hope of completing your investigation on crutches. The evidence that you have would be torn to pieces in a court-room by a good lawyer.

9

The factory in France is old-fashioned and in fact has only two customers outside mainland France. You go over to Rheims and eliminate all the internal customers as possible sources of the explosive used in your bomb, because all users of explosives have to keep very good records and theirs are complete and account for all their explosives. Of the two external customers, one is in Libya, the other in the Ivory Coast. You do not feel inclined to make the long trip to the Ivory Coast in person, so you get in touch with your friends at the Deuxième Bureau, the French secret service, who put you in contact with the relevant department. It becomes plain to you that the Ivory Coast can be discounted, so next you look into Libya. Turn to **148**.

10

You tell Gerald Cohen you have been looking for him, and why. He admits to being the one who told the police constable about the bomb in the bag, but seems very reluctant to say any more, until you ask his elder brother to leave. Then at last you get the full story out of him:

> 'I was on my way to the Bank of Suez at the time, and I was stopped by a man with a sort of German accent, who asked me whether I wanted to earn £20. I asked him what for. "I want you to tell a policeman that there is a bomb at the Bank of England," he replied. "Don't be daft," I said. "Nein," he said, "there really is something there, but I don't want to tell the police myself, because I am a foreigner and don't want to spoil my holiday." Anyway, I agreed to do as he asked. I took the money, told the copper and whipped off before he could question me any more. Well, I was going on holiday, wasn't I? The German-sounding bloke was about forty years old, very red-faced, and he wore one of those funny hats with a small feather in it. Maybe he was Swiss?'

You warn Gerald that he may be required to give his evidence in court some time, but also wish him an enjoyable holiday. Mark 53 on the Web and turn to **224**.

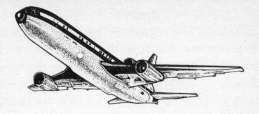

11

As soon as the door is fully open, you yell, 'Now!'
You both light your cylinder nozzles. Your plan
works: there is an explosion and the man with the
gun falls back. You are ready, and you jump on him
with your cylinder blazing. Klaus grabs the fallen
gun and shoots at the second man, who is still
several yards away. He falls wounded and drops his
weapon. You are now outside and running for the
weapon. You scoop it up and fall flat on the ground
– not a moment too soon, since more firing breaks
out. There must be a third man! You shoot towards
the flashes of gunfire in the darkness and the firing
stops. You hear the sounds of the man retreating
down the hillside.

All is quiet now, but you and Klaus stay alert until
you hear a helicopter arriving and see its vast
searchlight. It is the Italian mountain police. When
all the excitement has died down and the two
wounded men, one badly burned, have been taken
off by helicopter under arrest, you explain what
happened. The police in turn tell you that they were

able to arrive so promptly because they had been watching the kidnappers. While you and Klaus were dealing with some of the gang up here, they were capturing the rest down at the foot of the mountain. They are well pleased, because they were able to rescue the kidnap victims, who were lying in the back of the laundry van the kidnappers were using as cover.

Peter Klaus and yourself hire a truck, load the balloon and drive back to Basle. It is incredible how much camaraderie can be built up between people who share danger. On the way back, you say how much you hate terrorists. Klaus is thoughtful. 'No,' he says, half to himself, 'we would never do that.' You notice the word 'we' and say, 'But people do take risks: they steal, for instance.' 'Yes,' he says. 'But who says what "stealing" is? To a starving survivor of an aeroplane crash, maybe cannibalism is legitimate. As my friend Spinne argues, there are laws higher than man-made laws.' Mark *60* on the Web. If you have marked *3*, turn to **247**; otherwise, turn to **52**.

12

You fly ahead and arrange a reception committee for the men, if and when they arrive. It happens that you know the *souk*, or market, well, because you once rendered a service to some influential traders there. You find your old acquaintances, and they are only too glad to be of assistance. Together you concoct a plan . . .

The three criminals do land in Casablanca. It is evident that they do not know the place well and are confused by the hubbub. You had been counting on this. There are always crowds of young lads at the port asking, 'Carry your luggage?' or 'You want good hotel?' Given all the chaos, it is no trouble for your friends to divert the crooks into the crowded *souk*. Suddenly, one of them is pushed and jostled against a stall, which falls over. The place gets even noisier – but then goes deadly quiet when men pull out their knives. The three criminals reach into their pockets for their guns, only to find that their pockets have already been picked! The bemused English villains have no choice but to go where the knife-wielding locals force them. Turn to 56.

13

What your report has to tell you about the clock is this: it is a perfectly ordinary alarm clock, with a double bell and metal surround. It was set to ring twenty minutes before the explosion was due to occur. You sit back in your chair to contemplate this most peculiar fact. It is clear that the villains wanted to give plenty of warning, so that few or no people would be hurt if the bomb went off; the fact that a policeman was tipped off confirms this. Will you set in motion the process of tracing the clock (turn to **57**)? Or do you think that this fact could help you discover the motive for the crime (turn to **29**)?

14

What about opportunity? If you have marked on the Web *both 33 and 53*, turn to **228**. Otherwise, turn to **201**.

15

Because of the mountainous terrain of Switzerland, constructing nuclear-proof basements in new buildings requires both drilling machines and blasting explosive. The managing director of the Austrian factory is very co-operative and allows you access to any records you want. You find that there are six main wholesalers, each with different clients in different regions of Switzerland.

The six wholesalers supplied twenty clients in Switzerland during the last year. The records are all on file at the Austrian factory, because the wholesalers do not actually stock the explosive, but only take orders for it. They then pass on these orders to the Austrian factory, who supply the material to the clients. Turn to **180**.

16

Your holiday starts at the Mädel Lisa Inn, at the foot of the great Höchyi glacier. This is at the head of the Untersee valley, from which both the canton and the town get their name. You meet Klaus and find that he is well prepared with tents, sleeping-bags, climbing-boots, ice crampons, and so on. You start early in the morning because, as Klaus says, 'It is more better to cross the glacier before the sun she rises.' You take his word for it.

You make your way across slush ice, iron-hard ice and dirty ice-fields, and past ice in turrets like fairy castles; always under your feet you hear a tinkling and cracking and the babble of water. When you come to crevasses, you have to use the aluminium ladders Klaus supplied. At one point you come to a particularly deep one. Klaus breaks off a piece of ice with his pick and throws it down: it takes many seconds for it to finish falling. He tells you that in the past people have fallen in, and it has taken years for the body to appear at the base of the glacier. You dismiss the idea that this is a veiled threat: there is no way that Klaus could know who you really are.

Later you discover why he wanted to clear the glacier field before the sun reached its height: as the sun climbs, the surface becomes treacherous, and while your feet are cold and wet, your body is too hot. Moreover, the glare from the glacier is blinding, but you have sunglasses. Turn to **211**.

17

The days of careful work that this takes are all wasted. You do eventually track them down and eliminate them as possible suspects, but Scotland Yard takes you off the case, since you are taking too long and they are worried about the trail going cold.

18

If you have marked *40* on the Web, turn to **104**; otherwise, turn to **48**.

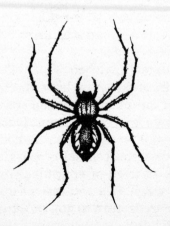

19

The Greek shipping company offered security for the loan of one of its ships. A very large sum of money is involved here, but the tycoon concerned has a great deal of wealth and is considered to be a very good risk. It is in fact perfectly normal for both aircraft and ships to be heavily mortgaged; otherwise, a lot of money would be tied up for a long time. Raising a loan gives the company cash for everyday matters. If you have not done so already, turn to **58** to check up on the Swiss loan or to **33** to check up on the Italian loan.

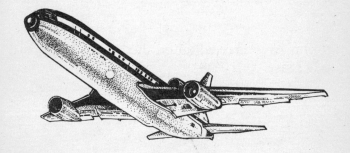

20

You carefully and silently leave the boat. You look around, but can see no one. You are very puzzled. You stay down low, but no one appears. Everything is silent, except for the sounds of wind, water and birds. There is a short stretch of grass leading up to a small copse in front of you; they could be hiding among the trees. Will you crawl through the long grass to the trees (turn to **30**), or return to the boat (turn to **63**)?

21

The cruiser pulls alongside the criminals' boat and a man with a suitcase goes aboard. You see that the fishing boats are starting to move in closer to the motor launch. Someone on board the launch presumably sees this too, because you hear a shout. The fishing vessels close in and uncover guns which they have mounted on their decks; the boats are manned by the Spanish naval police. They call out for the criminals to throw down their arms, and then they board the motor launch. A metal case is suddenly thrown into the water from the launch, but is recovered by naval divers who were already in place around the vessel.

It emerges later that the man in the cruiser was the international dealer whom the police in Lisbon were after. The Portuguese authorities are now able to raid his house, where they recover art treasures and other stolen goods. The Hatton Garden jewels were in the metal case. You are allowed to interrogate the crooks, but they vehemently deny being involved in the bomb at the Bank of England. As you should have guessed, it is not part of their MO. Mark 37 on the Web.

You may have recovered the stolen jewellery and received the reward money and the congratulations of the police, but you are no nearer knowing the motive behind the crime you are supposed to be investigating. Will you next look into the strange behaviour of the Securicor van (turn to 242) or into the missing bonds (turn to 164)? If you want to pursue another avenue of investigation altogether, turn to **200**.

22

You find, to your astonishment, that the Eagle operates from Cambridge! He never commits any crime in this country, so the most the authorities can do is co-operate with other countries on actual proof – but of course there rarely is any. You go to your friends in Special Branch and the Diplomatic Information Service and find the name of an agent in Cambridge. His job is to co-ordinate surveillance on the Eagle; he is a tutor in moral philosophy at one of the colleges. You drive to Cambridge, call up the agent and go along to his college to talk to him about the Eagle. He laughs and tells you that he will introduce you to him later. He gets out his file on the Eagle and leaves you to read it. Turn to **61**.

23

The timer proves to be a precision form of parking meter; in fact, most parking meters are quite precise, and are therefore popular among bombers. The mechanism had been modified by someone with good manual skills, and was set to go off at 10.10 a.m. The timer was originally made in Liechtenstein. An attempt had been made to obliterate the serial number of the timer with acid. The marks left by the acid were then painted over to disguise them. But the police laboratory technicians are very efficient: the paint aroused their suspicions, and they scraped it off and found the etching marks left by the acid. Examination through polarized light showed up the obliterated number, so it becomes a matter of wading through records to trace the source of the timer. Turn to **119**.

24

You travel to Basle, where Peter Klaus lives and operates as a guide. You decide to hire him as a guide: this seems the best way to get close to him. You contact him, posing as a writer on a fact-finding tour of Switzerland. He offers you the choice of a climbing holiday (turn to **16**) or a trip in a hot-air balloon (turn to **66**).

25

Tim Mayers is the person responsible for signing all documents in the section relating to loans and securities; no movements in or out should take place without his knowledge. He is twenty-eight years old, well respected and reliable; he is never late for work, always leaves on time, and takes his holidays at the expected times. Banks, as you know, are always suspicious of people who stay late and do not take holidays.

A check on his financial position reveals that Mayers lives at a rate very much higher than is warranted by the salary he earns at the bank. This makes your detective's antennae tingle, but further examination of his affairs shows that both he and his wife possess independent means, which are more than sufficient to meet his commitments. In fact, he seems to work not because he needs to, but because he enjoys it. You turn to consider John Colby, the bank messenger, who also had access to the safe during the relevant period. Turn to **114**.

26
The Lion strolls through Hamburg as if he owned it, or as if he had no cares in the world. You follow him through the notorious red-light district of the city to the docks of the River Elbe. You are being given a grand tour of the seedy side of the city. As you watch from the shadows of a doorway, he looks around furtively and slips into a warehouse, whose giant double doors are open a fraction. Will you go up to the warehouse to peep inside (turn to **271**) or wait where you are (turn to **199**)?

27
You wait until the following morning for a flight to Madeira. When you arrive, as a courtesy you introduce yourself to the local police in the capital, Funchal. You have already found out from Immigration at the airport that your quarries have arrived and what their address is: a villa in the mountains. You book into a hotel and arrange for a car with a driver to pick you up in the morning.

You suspect that the informant who told you about the gang may also have told the gang about you: this is the way with informers. So, while being driven to the villa, you are watching the way ahead with binoculars, and you see a flash of light, which may be another pair of binoculars reflecting the sun! You tell the driver to pull up, and you both take cover at the side of the road. Soon a car drives at speed down the road towards where you are. As it passes yours, you hear the distinctive sound of an Uzi machine-pistol being fired at the back seat of your car and at the tyres. It all happens in an instant, and then they are gone. You check on your driver: he is okay, but frightened. The car is a write-off. Will you hitch-hike up the road to the villa, to search it (turn to **160**), or back to Funchal (turn to **257**)?

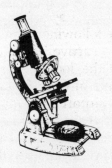

28

You spend days trying to worm relevant information out of the local populace and canton authorities, all of whom prove to be highly unco-operative. Eventually, you give up and return to

London in despair: what can you do against a wall of silence? You tell Scotland Yard what you have learned, but also inform them that you think the case will have to go on their 'unsolved' file. As for you, you cannot afford to continue with such an unproductive case any longer: you withdraw your services.

29

All crimes must have a motive. One motive is to gain money, power or position, or to put pressure on somebody or something in order to make such gain. Then there are crimes of passion, incited by the desire, for instance, to be avenged on someone. From the evidence at your disposal, do you think that this crime's motive is gain (turn to 121) or revenge (turn to 42), or is it to put pressure on the bank for some political, private or commercial reason (turn to 166)?

30

You creep carefully through the grass. Still no one appears, nor can you hear anything that could be human in origin. Suddenly an engine roars. You wheel around to see the boat moving away. You rush back to the jetty – but too late: the boat is gone. All this is very peculiar indeed, and not a little sinister. They must have been hiding in the engine-room, but what were they doing before? It seems that your life is not in danger, because they could certainly have killed you on the way here, while you were unconscious. Turn to 205.

It is seven days before you can attract attention. A boat passes by; it does not stop, but within an hour a police launch arrives at the island. They collect you, but also search the island, as though looking for something in particular. They seem to be treating you with suspicion, and you find that your passport and wallet are gone, so you have no means of identification. When you catch a glimpse of yourself in the mirror of the washroom, you are not so surprised that the police are wary of you; but still there seems to be more to it than that . . .

They do eventually find what they are looking for. Tucked into the roots of a tree is a cache of several thousand barbiturate tablets, a pistol and a healthy wad of money. However much you protest, the police do not believe your story about plots and kidnapping. You demand to be taken to Untersee, but no one there acknowledges that they have ever seen you before. You are deported back to England in disgrace, and Scotland Yard promptly take you off the case. You have not been getting on with the case for a week, as far as they are concerned, and you seem to have got involved in some shady drug-dealing yourself. They can do without that sort of trouble.

32

The cheese, it transpires, was from the valley of Untersee in Switzerland, and had been stored in Zurich before being transported. But it also turns out that Untersee is Ulrich's home, and that he was free in London at a crucial period – the day before the bomb was planted. He had arranged a day off work, so that he could see the sights. You ask how you can get in touch with Ulrich now, but they inform you that he is out on a job at the moment. Will you find out where he is and then go there, despite the time it would take (turn to 45), or will you pursue some other line of inquiry? If you pursue some other line, mark 23 on the Web and turn to 200.

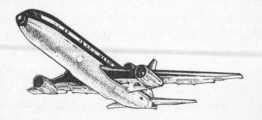

33

The bank tells you that the Italian loan, which was needed for expansion of business, has only just been made and is in the process of being split further. The bank considers the Italian business to be a very good risk indeed. Will you now look into the Greek loan (turn to 19) or the Swiss loan (turn to 58)?

When you arrive in Manchester, you ring the robbery squad, whom you have already told to expect you; they have traced Gunn to his brother-in-law's flat in Salford. You take a taxi to the address, where you find a rather obvious plain-clothes policeman waiting across the street. You ignore him and knock at the door. When it opens you ask to see Thomas Gunn. His relatives, who have clearly spotted the detective across the street, are delighted to get rid of you by telling you that he has left for Manchester airport, where he is about to catch a flight to go on holiday in Madeira.

You ring the airport to see if he can be stopped, but the airport police tell you that the plane is past boarding and unless you have a warrant to arrest him, they are in no position to do anything. He cleared Customs and Immigration with no problem. Turn to **172**.

35

'You must be prepared to fight to the last man,' he continues. 'You have seen our valley: is it not worth defending? You have seen our houses, the doors they are always open. You probably did not notice it, but we were watched all the way up the mountains. If we were not vigilant, how could we save tourists? We always watch and we always have to be prepared. The mountains have no mercy.' 'It seems to me,' you say, 'as though you would do anything to defend your valley.' 'Oh, yes,' he says, and then to himself, 'and have done.' You remember his look when you saw the avalanche scar and you say, 'Did many die in the avalanche?' 'Two,' he says. 'Both friends. But that was the least of it: it has almost killed our valley.' You look at him with a questioning look. 'Oh, yes,' he says. 'It does look good. If you only knew . . . but we are safe for a time.' Then he abruptly says, 'Time to sleep.' He extinguishes the lamp and that's that. Mark *60* on the Web. If you have marked 3, turn to **84**; otherwise, turn to **117**.

36

It could take for ever to trace all the messengers used by all the firms in the Stock Exchange, but it occurs to you that the name the young man used – John Kaham – might give a clue: it sounds Jewish. You therefore send out inquiries for a Jewish messenger who fits the description and who could have been in the vicinity of the Bank of England at the crucial time. The porters at the Stock Exchange are especially helpful. You end up with two possibilities. The first is James Cherkhom, aged seventeen, who works for Ponders and Blanding; the second is Gerald Cohen, aged sixteen and a half, who works for Peabody, King and Loeb. Will you first interview Cherkhom (turn to **107**) or Cohen (turn to **153**)?

37

You get in touch with those who know the Lion's haunts and habits, and discover that he is in Hamburg. You can hardly just ring him up for a chat on the phone: if you want to meet him, you must travel to Hamburg. This would take time. If you think it is worth it, turn to **245**. Otherwise, you may investigate the Eagle (turn to **22**), the Vulture (turn to **130**), Dutch terrorist groups (turn to **145**) or the Baader–Meinhoff gang (turn to **230**). If you have finished exploring the possibility that there is some terrorist connection to the bomb at the Bank of England, you can get in touch with your criminal underworld informants (turn to **83**) or the manufacturers of the explosive (turn to **261**). If you have finished looking into the explosive and want to change tack altogether, turn to **200**.

You make arrangements to take the car on to Nice. As you drive along, you reflect that Ulrich must have continued on the *autostrada* and that you probably overtook him on the road! The journey to Nice is travelled on much slower roads: you have time to enjoy the scenery. The Apennine mountains loom in the distance; you cross the plain beside the River Po and then you come to the Alpes Maritimes, the mountains which divide Italy and France. Now you are on the mountainous road which snakes around hairpin bends as it descends towards the city of Nice.

As you wind your way towards France and Nice, you pass a nasty accident, with a car on its side up against the mountain rock-face. An ambulance and two police cars are already in attendance, so there is no need for you to stop. A short while later, they speed past you, with their headlights blazing and sirens screaming. When you get to Nice, you contact the police to tell them what you are doing. They look puzzled at first, but you soon find out why. It turns out that Ulrich was a witness to the road accident you passed, and is still at the police station, making a statement. No wonder the police gave you strange looks when you started mentioning his name: they must have thought you were psychic or something! Turn to 214.

39

Armed with introductions from the relevant Swiss authorities, you go to Untersee and ask to see the records. Switzerland maintains thorough records on all its citizens. You discover that Dieter, who you know is an engineer, is working on repairing damage caused by an avalanche the previous year. As both excavation and blasting are necessary for this work, it is obvious that he has both access and skill where explosives are concerned. Will you check on the explosives record (turn to **86**) or go to the works site (turn to **78**)?

40

Dieter Francchi was staying at the Waverley Hotel, quite near the City of London. You ring the hotel and find that on the morning of the bomb scare he had an early breakfast and left the hotel at about 8.30. The doorman remembers him by his green hat with a little feather in it. So Francchi fits Cohen's description of the man who told him about the bomb. He left London the next day. You go to the hotel to make more in-depth inquiries.

The hotel takes photocopies of all passports: Francchi turns out to be a mining engineer, from the canton of Untersee in Switzerland. He made two phone calls while he was at the hotel: one was local, the other to Basle in Switzerland. On the day in question, he had the English breakfast at 7.45, which he had booked the night before. His key was handed in and he left the hotel at about 8.30. He returned at about 11.30, then unexpectedly cancelled his room and left by taxi for the airport the next day. The porter remembers the man because he tipped well. Turn to **139**.

41

You wander around for days, following leads that go nowhere and constantly meeting with a blank wall of silence from the local population. Eventually, Scotland Yard take you off the case, calling you 'T. S. the Time Spender'; but by then you are just about ready to take yourself off the case anyway.

42

One of the strongest motives for crime is that of revenge for some real or imagined hurt or damage. It therefore makes sense for you to consider this as a motive for the bomb scare. The Bank hands over to you their file on the subject. It has three parts. The first part deals with former employees of the Bank who thought they had been badly done by; the second part covers those who think that the Bank has been responsible for some personal misfortune of theirs; and the third part deals with all those who feel that the Bank is responsible for the ills of the country or even the world. If you start with the first part, turn to 134; if you check into the second part, turn to 154; if you start with the third part, turn to 226.

43

You return to the UK with the gold rings and chains. You are thankful that the thieves did not have time to melt the stuff down, as there is no way to identify a lump of gold. You go to Scotland Yard, where the Assistant Commissioner (Crime) sends for you. He thanks you for the capture of the gang, and assures you that the reward for the recovery of the jewellery will be yours – but then he goes on to tell you off for interfering in cases that are no concern of yours. Nor is he very happy about the method used to extract information from the villains. The long and short of it is that Scotland Yard feel that they no longer require your services in investigating the bomb at the Bank of England.

44

It is very eerie on the site, with all the huge machinery unnaturally quiet, and piles of unidentifiable objects in the darkness. You jiggle the locks on the doors of the huts, but they are secure. Without knowing it, you have set off an alarm which rings in the Untersee police station. You try to look into the buildings, through the windows, but as it is dark, and you do not wish to use your torch for fear of being spotted, you cannot really see anything.

Judging by the size of the filing cabinets, you have just discovered the hut which holds the plans of the site when you are caught in the headlights of the three police cars which have crept up to the site. You are arrested for trespass and intent to burglarize. When Scotland Yard hears of your nefarious deeds, they take you off the case, to prevent further international embarrassment. You try to convince them that you have the makings of a case, but you find that while you were being held in the Untersee police station much of the incriminating evidence was being disposed of. You have failed.

45
You find that Ulrich is in the middle of a journey which has taken him to Yugoslavia. He is scheduled to return via Italy, and should arrive in Florence tomorrow. You fly over to Florence. The flight is uneventful, but when you arrive in Florence, the first thing that happens is that the plane is kept on the runway for two hours. There is a bomb threat in the terminal, and it takes that length of time before it is considered safe to unload the passengers. Then, on the way into town your car, thoughtfully provided by the local police, gets a flat tyre, and it turns

out that the spare also has a puncture. All in all, it takes you six hours to reach the centre of town. Then you start to try to find the company where Ulrich is due to make his delivery, but neither the driver nor anyone he contacts on the radio seems to know the place. Eventually, you resort to the telephone directory and find the address that way. Turn to **69**.

46

You decide to return to the issue which first reported the avalanche the day after it happened, but it contains no more than a dramatic write-up of the event and obituaries of the two people who died. However, an article in an issue a few weeks after that is more interesting:

Given the importance of cheese to the canton's livelihood, we thought that our readers may be interested in a report from the Geneva Biological Research Unit, whose gist is as follows: During the last two years, considerable research has been undertaken with regard to specialist cheeses such as Roquefort, Limberg, Camembert and others. The micro-organisms responsible for each cheese are in fact very specific and the species differ from cave to cave. It has been found that, for them to thrive, temperature and humidity must remain within a very limited range. The correct conditions are found in deep caves, provided that they are not subject to sudden changes of ventilation and provided that the general content of the minor chemical constituents of the air in the caves is conducive.

It has proved possible to reproduce the micro-organisms in the laboratory. However, caverns remain the best environment, because the general atmosphere and even the walls are generally found to be saturated with the appropriate organisms. It is presumably for this reason that genetic drift does not occur, and the same cheese is produced year after year. But where conditions in the caves have been changed to a certain extent, it may take as long as two years for stable conditions to be re-established.

Vintage cheeses for vintage wines?

Mark 51 on the Web and turn to **147**.

47

All the laboratory can tell you is that extremely sensitive spectro-analytical instruments detected the slight aroma of cheese, and that this was more noticeable on the outside of the bag than on the inside. Of course, there are plenty of traces of plastic explosive and so on, but this tiny whiff of cheese is the only unexpected factor about the bag. Mark *48* on the Web and turn to **200**.

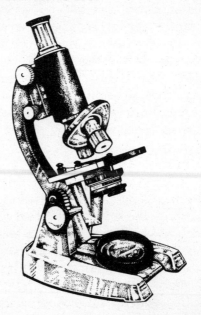

48

You try to poke around the Swiss security forces. Your office receives a reprimand from the Foreign Office, who have had a complaint from the Swiss government. Your contract is terminated.

49

You interview the security staff at Lloyd's and the description you give them seems to fit a seventeen-year-old messenger called John Cook. The porter in charge of him says that he has been sent to Richmond with some urgent papers and is expected back soon. This sounds hopeful, so you decide to wait, rather than going to the Stock Exchange to investigate the other possibility; but in fact Cook calls in later from a hospital – he has been knocked off his motor scooter. You go to see him at the hospital. His girlfriend is by his bedside and confirms that they were together at the time of the bomb alert. They seem to be truthful. However, Cook says that he knows a Stock Exchange messenger called Jerry (he doesn't know the surname) who answers the description. Mark 2 on the Web and turn to 36.

50

You turn to Interpol to get more information about the Italian with the shady past. You find that he was under suspicion of having killed a Mafia boss. His daughter had been in hospital for two months before the crime was committed and Interpol thinks that she had been kidnapped and that a rescue attempt had ended in the shooting incident. You ask Interpol if there is any Swiss connection and they say that they think the whole operation was mounted from the Swiss side of the Italian border. You go back to the bank to see if you can gain any more information on this Italian, but the most astonishing thing you learn is that Spinne's account has been closed! He is slipping even further out of your grasp.

You remember the name of the Englishman who backed the account and you go to see him. He lives in the country and is definitely one of the upper crust. You ask him why he backs the account. He says, 'I don't any more: it has been closed.' You persist, and the Englishman eventually says, 'Wolf Spinne is a great man. I admire him, and since as a shoemaker he cannot do all that he would like to do, I provide him with funds.' You ask whether he is afraid that Spinne might take advantage. He laughs and says, 'I know that you have seen the account and that you know how much has been taken out of it, so don't ask silly questions. Spinne is a man of honour.' You ask whether he is also a criminal. The Englishman sets his jaw and says, 'I don't care if he is or if he isn't: he has done me a great service.' And that is all you can get out of him. If you have marked 51 on the Web, turn to **187**; otherwise, turn to **223**.

51

Inquiries indicate that no suspicion at all can be attached to Pauli. Although he would have the technical expertise to assemble a bomb, he was working at the Swiss embassy on the morning of the bomb scare. Will you now investigate Francchi (turn to **40**) or Maerling (turn to **188**)? Alternatively, you could return to **73** and choose another category of Swiss visitor to look into or, if you haven't already done so, check up on Austrian (turn to **60**) or German (turn to **163**) visitors. If you have had enough of checking up on tourists, turn to **200**.

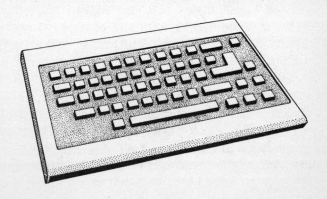

52

You make your way back to Untersee and decide to visit the bar of your hotel: it is popular among the locals, and may be a good place to pick up more information. In the bar, it seems that everyone has already heard about what happened, and you are pestered by questions, rather than having the opportunity to ask any of your own. Not only that, but you are also bought quite a few drinks. You find that, while you are not drunk, your tongue has become a little unguarded, and you are saying things that a visitor should perhaps not know about Klaus. Will you stop drinking altogether, which might look a bit peculiar (turn to **106**), or accept another drink, but sip it slowly and make it last (turn to **189**)?

53

You receive a longer report about Heinrich Popper two days later. It includes individual reports from security, the police, his local canton and the army, since all Swiss males between sixteen and sixty serve for some weeks with the army each year. Security says that the man is just noisy, but no real problem. Police records indicate drunkenness, disorderly behaviour and breaches of the peace, but there is no record of actual physical violence. Their opinion is that Heinrich just likes excitement and goes out of his way to create it. The local authorities obviously do not dislike Popper and their report is positively in his favour. This is backed up by the army report, which indicates that as a soldier he is first-class and would in his superior's opinion be a definite asset where actual warfare was concerned. His only problem as far as the army is concerned is that he is easily bored, so they wisely keep him very busy during his periods of service. Mark *18* on the Web. If you still need to read about Schmidt, turn to **270**; if you still need to read about Klaus, turn to **186**; if you have now read what the report has to say about all three of them, mark *32* on the Web and turn to **200**.

54

The question here is whether the bomb was so placed that, had it gone off, it would have given access to money or valuables. You go over the premises yourself and ask for a full security report. Exhaustive examination of the place shows that neither money nor valuables would have become vulnerable, and that in fact the normal activities of the bank would hardly have been disrupted. Mark *4* on the Web and turn to **79**.

55

You decide it is time to move further up your tunnel. In the darkness, your foot strikes a stone, and the tunnel magnifies the sound. With so many tunnels, and with the strange echoes, you judge that it will be difficult to locate the source of the noise, but no doubt they will try hard, if they think that it was caused by a human intruder, not just some animal or natural slippage of loose rock.

Within a short time, the whole place seems to be full of searching people. You lie very low, making sure that your face and hands are hidden. You know very well that they usually show up and give away the position of someone who is trying to hide. You crawl quietly even further up your tunnel, once you are sure that there is no one in your immediate vicinity. Turn to **221**.

56

They find themselves pushed into a cellar, where they are forced to empty their pockets. All the contents are brought to you and you find keys to cases and the safe on the boat which they had hired. You go to the boat. In the false bottom of one suitcase, you find the stolen loot. Meanwhile, your Moroccan friends have extracted a confession from the criminals. You suspect that they did not ask politely for the information, but you believe now that you will be able to send them to prison. Turn to **43**.

You decide to trace the clock. It is intact, so you have the maker's name and inside you find the inspection number and the date of manufacture. You contact the manufacturers by phone and they are most anxious to assist the police in their inquiries: you forget to tell the woman you are speaking to that, strictly speaking, you are not the police. Anyway, she gives you the access code to their warehouse computer and you start work at your terminal.

You find that the batch to which your clock belonged was produced to fill a large order from Woolworth's. You equip yourself with the details of packing-case number and quantity and get in touch with Woolworth's main store, from which all goods are sent out to the regional stores. The person you speak to is reluctant to allow you access to private company records, but you know how to deal with that. You ask to be put through to the Marketing Director, and you explain to him how you feel sure his company would wish to do all it could to serve the interests of the community. He agrees absolutely and, when you are returned to the main store, you get full co-operation! You are given their computer access codes, and a few minutes after you have fed in your requirements your printer chatters into life. Turn to **82**.

58

If this is the third loan you are looking into, mark 69 on the Web. What is curious about this loan is that nearly the whole amount of the loan was in the one parcel in the bank's safe, which is uncommon practice, because it is a bad idea. You wonder how it happened in the first place. The loan was made about two years ago, and in the normal course of events the bonds would have been scattered all over the banking system by now. The loan was a municipal loan guaranteed by local citizens and by the local government. This set-up makes it a really safe loan. Turn to **89**.

59

If you have marked 3 on the Web, turn to **183**; if you have marked 68 on the Web, turn to **101**; if you have marked neither of these, turn to **41**; if you have marked both, turn to **225**.

Of the five single males, one is in hospital with a broken leg, which was broken the day before the bomb scare, so you can rule him out; and another has also been bed-ridden, with a virus. The remaining three also come to nothing. One is visiting a girlfriend and, according to the landlady, 'They never leave the flat.' Of the other two, one is a policeman on holiday, so he is unlikely to be a suspect; and the other has a beard, so he can be eliminated, since a beard does not figure in Cohen's description.

There are seven males in the family groups, but inquiries do not throw up anything suspicious. They seem to spend their time seeing the sights and escorting their families around.

There are forty males who recently entered the country on residents' visas; all of them were cleared initially by the Home Office and the police. What you already know eliminates those with beards and moustaches, those over six foot, those who limp and those whose English is very good. You are left with two men who could answer the description. One of these was at work in Potters Bar all day on the day in question. The other looks like a possibility on paper, but turns out to be too thin to fit Cohen's description.

All of the six males in the relevant age-group among the Austrian tourist parties were in two coach parties which went to Stonehenge and Stratford-upon-Avon respectively on the day in question.

So you have drawn a blank with the Austrians.
Mark 1 on the Web. If you now want to investigate
the Swiss visitors, turn to **73**; if you check up on the
Germans, turn to **163**. If you have had enough of
checking up on tourists, turn to **200**.

61
You read that the real name of the Eagle is Ramos
Pojeros. His parents disappeared during the
Brazilian Dirty War. He was educated in Brazil, but
after his parents' disappearance relatives sent him
to an English private school. After school, he went
to Cambridge and acquired a degree in Sociology
and Anthropology. As part of his degree he spent a
year with the Huk insurgents in the Philippines,
which was when his revolutionary tendencies were
confirmed. He was trained in Libya by the CIA and
in Jordan with the PLO. He is sober of habits, and
highly intelligent. The character report concludes
that he is *very* dangerous, because he is rarely out of
control: he knows his own limits. He has a hatred
for any form of authority. He runs a very tight ship,
as far as his group is concerned, and is a meticulous
planner of operations, most of which cannot be
directly traced to him: he never commits anything to
writing or any other form of record. He is both
feared and respected by other terrorists. Turn to
179.

62

Government control over explosives in Austria is extremely good and there is no sign that any have gone astray or been stolen, so now you turn your attention to the Swiss outlet. Turn to **15**.

63

You wait on the boat for what seems like an interminable length of time. But their patience is thinner than yours, and they emerge from the engine-room where they were hiding and storm the cabin where you are waiting, bottle in hand. There are only two of them, and they have to enter the cabin one at a time, so it is relatively easy for you to overcome them. You tie them up and return to the mainland: you find that you are near the city of Lausanne. Mark *68* on the Web. Do you think the authorities in Lausanne can offer you any help (turn to **115**), or will you return to Untersee as if nothing had happened (turn to **59**)?

64

The police file on Jimbo informs you that he often travels to Ipswich and usually stays at the Pegasus pub there. You go there and explain to the manager that you are looking for Jimbo. The landlord says that you have missed him: he has gone off to Cambridge to visit friends. When you get to Cambridge, you soon find that the address the manager gave you is false. But luckily the police are more helpful: they recognize a photo of Jimbo that you have as a Mr James, who runs a stall in the market. They say that they have wondered about him, because he is so often away from his stall. But they have an address for Mr James in the village of Little Abney. Will you go there (turn to 98), or will you give up this time-consuming chase? If you give up, you may investigate either the Securicor van (turn to 242) or the missing bonds (turn to 164).

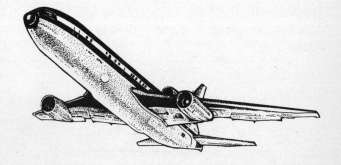

You decide to look into Maria Kirk because she used a garage's notepaper to write to the Bank, so she might conceivably have the expertise to make a bomb. Inquiries with the Home Office security computer reveal further that she had once trained as a mining engineer, and so would be expected to know something about explosives. You pay her a visit at the East London garage where she is working as a mechanic. You find that she has a three-month-old baby near her even while she works; and her workmates confirm her alibi.

You feel that you are treading on the margins of terrorism with this third part of the file. If you have not already done so, you may wish to look into the possibility that the bomb was planted or supplied by terrorists (turn to 113). If you want to look into the other parts of the file, consisting of those who hold personal grudges against the Bank, turn to 134 for former employees or to 154 for the rest. If you have finished with this line of inquiry and want to investigate another possible motive, turn to 29 and choose again.

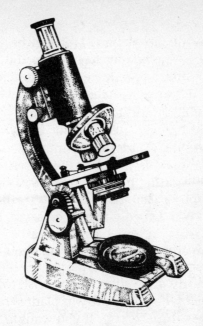

66

In the morning everything is ready for going up in
the hot-air balloon. You have come dressed in warm
clothing, as Klaus told you. He warns you now that
hot-air ballooning in the Alps can be dangerous,
because the thermals are occasionally very chaotic,
with many down-draughts caused by glaciers in
shadow and other reasons for sudden turbulence.
You do in fact already know this, and have hoped
that stress might cause him to give away information. You take off. It is a glorious day. There is
room to move around the gondola, despite your
luggage and equipment, such as cylinders of gas
and stand-by burners.

The scenery is spectacular, with its snow-capped heights, wooded valleys and many more rivers than you had imagined. When you are above the clouds, they look as though they are the landscape of a fairy-tale alpine world. Somehow it reminds you of something you feel you once knew – those 'mountains' so tall and solid-looking, but in fact just mist. In places the clouds boil up into tall columns: Klaus explains that this indicates the presence of thermals. You are drifting towards Italy. You check that you have your passport, and you ask about Customs and so on. 'I filed papers', he says, 'in Italy, Germany, Austria and Liechtenstein. With a balloon you can end up anywhere or nowhere.'

You are so absorbed by the view that you are in danger of forgetting your purpose: anything worldly seems insignificant by comparison with the eternity of the Alps. But you recollect yourself and start up a conversation: 'To think I was in London only a week ago, with rain and damp bricks and soggy sheets of paper blowing around.' Turn to **173**.

67

You take the coast road from Valencia to Alicante, which is fairly windy, but you make good time on the straight stretches. However, at one left-hand bend, your sense of danger must have deserted you, because you run into the side of the road. You scrape the whole length of the car on some rocks, and lose a car door in the process. When you emerge, shaken, from the car, you find that you have damaged the suspension as well. You kick the car in disgust, when you really feel like kicking yourself. By the time you have extricated yourself from the police inquiries, you have lost several vital hours. Turn to **158**.

68

While all the official wheels are grinding into motion, you decide to check further into Wolf Spinne, whose name means 'spider'. You know that he was in London at the time of the bomb, and you know that he was an associate of the criminals, but you do not have enough evidence to convict him of anything. You remember what struck you as odd before: that despite being a shoemaker he seemed to be far from short of money. You return to the hotel he stayed at in London. Turn to **217**.

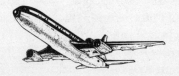

69

By the time you are able to get in touch with the place, the only news awaiting you is that Ulrich has been and gone. He is now on his way to Milan with cargo, some of which will be unloaded there, while the rest is scheduled for Nice, in France. Will you give up this Italian trip as a fiasco and return to England (turn to 6), or will you follow Ulrich to Milan (turn to 184)?

70

You miss the actual train which the stranger caught, but another one leaves shortly. This will not take you all the way to Zurich, but will allow you to make a connection with the sleeper at Stuttgart. When you make the connection, you realize that this sleeper must be the one which the stranger caught! When you board the train, you soon find him. He is awake and has moved from his sleeping-compartment to a regular passenger compartment.

You sit down in the same compartment, and the train soon pulls out of the station. He seems to be friendly and speaks good English. You strike up a conversation. He gives his name as Herr Schwimmer. The conversation turns to computers, and you find that he is an engineer and very knowledgeable and entertaining on the subject. Then you start to talk about politics and scandal: he seems to know a great deal about the affairs of politicians and media people. Turn to **174**.

The criminals have quite a start on you. Will you hire a light aircraft (turn to **274**) or a fast boat equipped with radar (turn to **133**)?

In the morning, well rested, you get ready to move down the mountain. You keep close to the edge of the avalanche scar, but you know that you need to keep hidden. The valley is full of eyes and you are sure that, if it becomes known that you are interested in the avalanche, people might prevent you doing what you have set out to do. The lower you get, the more carefully you have to move: you are surprised by the number of times you have to take cover. There seem to be people everywhere – children, woodmen, even walkers like yourself. The descent is at times very slippery, but you make reasonable progress.

On one occasion, however, when you are trying to hide from a group of three children out with their dogs, you slip down the bank of a stream and end up soaked to the waist by icy-cold water. There is a barn near by, whose upper level has a big, open hatch into which the sun is shining. You could hide in the barn and dry out (turn to **140**), or you could press on and hope that perhaps the exercise will dry you out (turn to **203**).

73

Swiss male visitors to London in the relevant age-range fall into four categories for the period you are interested in. If you want to investigate single visitors, turn to **93**. If you want to investigate family groups, turn to **236**. If you want to investigate those who came with a tourist party, turn to **7**. If you want to investigate those who have come on a resident's permit, but have not yet been in this country for more than eight weeks, turn to **206**.

74

You are blindfolded and taken to the house where the injured terrorist is being held. You tell the psychiatrist what you want to know. After six hours he returns and says that the terrorist thought he saw a bloke carrying a brown-paper bag up Bartholomew Lane the morning of the bomb. He remembered it because he laughed at the funny-looking hat, which seemed somehow incongruous with the paper bag. Will you now investigate the Hatton Garden robbery (turn to **2**) or the missing bonds (turn to **164**)?

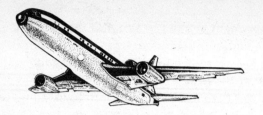

75

The drivers are being interviewed separately, and since both you and the police are convinced that they are lying about something, you keep up the pressure. You use the information gained from the tachograph as a lever, and get an admission that the three of them did in fact visit the Blackwater River. They insist that this was just for the purpose of resting and sight-seeing, but, since you know that the part of the estuary that they must have stopped at is clogged with the rusting hulks of old ships, you can easily disprove that story.

When the true tale emerges, you find that their job was to throw waterproof bales of smuggled goods overboard from the cross-channel ferry, which would be picked up by an English vessel, brought up the Blackwater, reloaded in the lorries and sold in Bristol. The police are delighted: a major smuggling ring seems to have been exposed. You are not so delighted: all this has nothing to do with bombs! Mark 70 on the Web. Will you now look into the Swiss lorry (turn to **131**) or the Austrian lorries (turn to **244**)?

76

As soon as he opens the door and sees your tent-tunnel, the kidnapper knows something is amiss. He steps back and starts shooting wildly through the doorway. Klaus grunts and falls back wounded. You ignite your cylinder, trying to cause an explosion, but by now the cool air has dispersed the gas. You hear the sound of footsteps running away down the hillside.

You make Klaus as comfortable as you can, but he is in some pain, and is muttering something which sounds like 'Tell it to the spinner'. You decide not to move him. You tell him you'll be back with help, and set off down the mountain. Turn to **162**.

77

Apart from what the police tell you, you also receive a phone call from one of your informants, who claims that the gang the police suspect was responsible for the robbery. Of course, none of this is evidence which will convict them, and you have to decide whether or not it is worth pursuing them, because there may be no connection between the robbery and the bomb scare except that of coincidence. If you decide to pursue this line of investigation, there are two possible courses of action: you could try to trace the gang's fence (turn to **112**), or you could try to track down the gang members themselves (turn to **210**). If you decide not to pursue this line of investigation, will you check up on the missing bonds (turn to **164**) or the Securicor van (turn to **242**)?

78

You try to get into the works site, but you are stopped and told that the matter is confidential. Well, perhaps it is secret government work, for all you know. You go back to your hotel to explore this possibility by phone, using contacts of yours in the Swiss security forces, but the operator tells you that the line is out of order. You go out into the town and make for a public phone kiosk which takes coins, but when you enter the booth you find that the phone has been vandalized. This is very peculiar, because as you approached the booth someone else stepped out of it: to your trained senses, he looked like an off-duty policeman. You hire a car and find that you are definitely being followed. However, you manage to lose your tail and get to a usable phone. Your security contact tells you that the works are definitely not part of any government operation. Turn to **275**.

79

There is certainly no sign that the Bank of England would have lost any money or even prestige as a result of the bomb. As far as you can see, the Bank was and is entirely unaffected by the bomb scare, apart from a minor hiccup in the exchange rate for sterling, which was soon rectified. The most notable fact is that the alarm clock was timed to go off well before the bomb, as if it was meant to give warning of the presence of the bomb. So it does look as though you should look elsewhere, not to the Bank itself, for an explanation for the crime. Turn to **150**.

80

It is not at all clear who had the opportunity to place the bomb. There are two possible leads: one is the teenager who gave the alarm; the other arises out of the preliminary police report, which includes the statement of several witnesses that a Securicor van was threading its way as quickly as possible through the rush-hour traffic of Threadneedle Street at approximately the time that the alarm was raised about the bomb. If you want to try to trace the teenager, turn to 229. If you want to investigate the Securicor van, turn to 242.

81

Have you satisfactorily completed your investigation into the means used in the crime? If you have marked on the Web *all* of 42, 48, 5 and 32, turn to 120. If you have not marked all these numbers, turn to 201.

82

The print-out shows that the batch as a whole was issued to the East Anglia area. There are eight stores in this area, but only one of them – the one in Harwich – has so far put the clocks on display. To be thorough, you should determine whether or not your clock has been stolen from one of the other stores before being put on display. Will you complete the investigation in this way (turn to 193), or will you take a risk and get in touch with the Harwich store straight away (turn to 209)?

You ring up your criminal 'grasses', or informers, to see if they have heard any whispers about the bomb. Nothing. You ask about sources of explosive and arrange to meet 'Joe the Bunce' at his usual place of business, a café in Petticoat Lane. You go there and sit down with a cup of coffee while you wait for him. He arrives, but is waylaid by someone who is trying to sell him some rings. You sip your drink, wondering if it's coffee or dishwater, and try not to watch the transaction. Eventually money changes hands and he pockets the rings. He comes over to you and you tell him what you want to know. He disappears to make a phone call. When he returns, he has a smile on his face and suggests that you meet later at a Soho club. If you decide to meet him, turn to **237**. Alternatively, if you have not already done so, you could check up on the manufacturers of the explosive (turn to **261**) or use your security contact to investigate the possibility that the bomb was planted or supplied by terrorists (turn to **113**).

84

The whole town is uncooperative; the avalanche injured the whole community in some way. This is beginning to look very like a motive: to judge by Klaus's words, he would not worry too much about breaking the law in order to preserve the community. Turn to **117**.

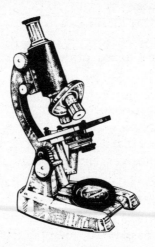

85

The next day you see what you can find out about Intercon. Fortunately, the company records are available to the public. The firm is a continental one which has spread to England and also, as other cleaning firms do, offers a wide range of security services. You ring Intercon's office and make an appointment with the area manager. You question him about who owns the company. He gives you a copy of the company's yearly reports and accounts, and leaves you to examine them. Among the continental directors, you notice the name of Liselle Goch – she is the only woman listed. Further questioning reveals that the company has a policy, unpleasant to careless employees, of having the directors make spot checks on the work. When they make these spot checks, it is usual for them to wear normal cleaner's overalls, so that the work-force are unaware of the identity of this new person on their team. Mark 55 on the Web. If you have marked 22 on the Web, turn to **200**; otherwise, turn to **125**.

86
You go to the office of Dieter's employers and ask to see the explosives book. It does not take much perusal to see that it would be very easy to build up a stock of explosives, simply by not using all that you have withdrawn from the stores. Mark 13 on the Web. You ask for access to the works records, but you can sense that these people are not being very co-operative. This feeling grows to a certainty when they refuse to give you any more information and refer you to the Town Council. Turn to **152**.

87
You already have Klaus on your list of suspects, so this is beginning to look extremely interesting. You find that both Francchi and Klaus arrived at the hotel in Amsterdam at the same time, though they did not acknowledge each other in public. The timing suggests that they may have arrived on the train from Frankfurt. You find that seats had been

reserved on this train for both of them, but in different carriages. A little more checking reveals that they had both come by train to Frankfurt the day before from Basle in Switzerland, where Klaus lives, as you know. Francchi, however, lives in Untersee. There is one question in your mind: why did they stop in Frankfurt? Mark 33 on the Web. It looks as if you have found two firm suspects here. If you want to investigate Swiss visitors further, turn to **73** and choose again. Or, if you haven't done so already, you may want to check up on the German (turn to **163**) or Austrian (turn to **60**) visitors. Otherwise, turn to **200**.

88

You wake up. You have no idea where you are. You cannot see and your head feels as though it is held in a vice: you cannot turn it. Then you realize that your eyes are covered, which is why you cannot see. You reach up with your hands to remove the covering, but a voice says, 'Keep still. You are in hospital.' You ask what the matter is and are told that you have a hairline crack in your skull and are suffering from concussion.

You have no choice but to remain in hospital for seven days. You try to get up after two days, but dizziness soon forces you back to bed. You are only partially recovered when the police pay you an official visit to tell you that you have been taken off the case. They wish you a speedy recovery, but they need someone to be working on the case now.

89

You check with Zurich and Geneva and find that the loan was taken out on behalf of the canton of Untersee in Switzerland, for the purpose of extending their co-operative cheese-making facility. Then you discover that the bank which originally negotiated the loan was Hessemann and Pinelli, which is Liselle Goch's parent bank. If you have marked 8 on the Web, turn to **182**. Otherwise, turn to **196**.

90

Popper is obviously a suspect. The report states that he advocates violent revolution, belongs to many political clubs, and is constantly getting involved in arguments with his friends, acquaintances, the authorities and even with his family. If you think he is too obvious, you can read what the report has to say about Schmidt (turn to **270**) or Klaus (turn to **186**), if you have not already done so. If you would like to request an in-depth report on Popper from the Swiss authorities, turn to **53**. If you do not want to pursue inquiries into these three any further, mark 32 on the Web and turn to **200**.

91

While the official wheels are grinding into motion, you review your case. The chief weakness seems to be related to this man Spinne, whose name means 'spider'; you have hearsay about him, but no evidence. You decide to check back through the tourist records to see if you can place him in London.

You find that Wolf Spinne, aged fifty-nine, whose profession is given as shoemaker, entered the country shortly before the time of the bomb, as a member of a tour party; but he left the party and so should, strictly speaking, have been reclassified as a 'Single Visitor'. You check the London hotel records and find the hotel he stayed at. To your surprise (since he is a shoemaker), it is an expensive one, and he is remembered at the hotel, which you telephone, as having spared no expense in the meals he ate as well. You decide to go to the hotel for further checking. Turn to **217**.

You contact MI6 through official channels and are told that they will co-operate because bomb threats are indeed a matter affecting the security of the realm. They give you clearance to ring their 'sanitation' department. You know that this is the department which has the job of cleaning up any mess left by security operations, such as damaged vehicles, injured or even dead agents, people who need hiding, bullet holes, and all evidence that needs to vanish before the police have to take official notice of what has been going on. You ring this department and are told that in this case the Securicor van was acting as an ambulance and had picked up an injured agent and a rather badly battered would-be terrorist. Mark 52 on the Web. If you want to hear more, turn to **273**. On the other hand, if you think that these are rather dangerous waters, and also probably nothing to do with the bomb at the Bank of England, then you can investigate either the Hatton Garden robbery (turn to **2**) or the missing bonds (turn to **164**). Finally, you could contact the Soviets, to see if they have any knowledge of the bomb (turn to **138**).

93

After elimination procedures based on Cohen's description, and by checking where in the country the single visitors went if they left London, you narrow the field down to three possibilities. Heinz Pauli is aged twenty-nine, with a stocky build and blue-green eyes; he works in the technical department of the Swiss Civil Service; his visit combined business with pleasure, since he was examining technical equipment at the Swiss embassy, but also went to the opera at Glyndebourne. Dieter Franchi is aged thirty-six, with a stocky build and grey eyes; he is a mining engineer; the purpose of his visit was for a general cultural holiday, visiting museums, galleries and so on. Karl Maerling is a research student at Stuttgart University; he was intending to do some research at the British Library towards his thesis, which is entitled 'The Cromwellian period as a precursor to European revolution'. If you choose to check up on Pauli, turn to **51**. Or will you investigate Franchi (turn to **40**) or Maerling (turn to **188**)?

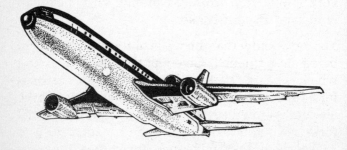

94

Once you are inside the cave mouth, you feel concealed enough to risk using a torch; you also brought spare bulbs and batteries. You look around and see that the entrance is due to be fitted with sliding doors; but the neat stonework around the entrance also continues inside the tunnel. You find that odd: why not just level the walls? You carry on down the tunnel and even forty feet from the entrance everything is masonry. Here they are still working on it, and you can see that it is backed by very strong iron-work, as though it is meant to withstand an earthquake.

You now know that the walls of the excavation are being strengthened. Given all the air-conditioning which is being fitted, perhaps all this work really is for a nuclear fall-out shelter. But then why put the air-conditioning *outside*? Ahead of you, the tunnel forks. Will you take the left-hand branch (turn to **126**) or the right-hand branch (turn to **135**)?

95

Accompanied by a park ranger, you set off into the mountains at ten o'clock the next day, having borrowed some climbing-boots. The scenery is terrific, but clouds are building up and thunder and lightning are forecast. The ranger mutters to himself and seems worried. Within minutes the storm is upon you, and you both shelter under some rocks. There is a sudden crack, and part of the rock-face falls away. You both get hit by broken rocks: you are only bruised, but a heavy rock falls on the ranger's leg. You lift it off him, but he is in a good deal of pain: he may have broken his ankle, you think. Will you leave him and go for help (turn to 141), or will you strap up his leg and attempt to get him down the mountain to the nearest village (turn to 124)?

96

You find that the Bank has received no implied threats, but it takes quite a time to discover this, since it involves a lot of interviewing. But, in the process, you also discover that the Bank has received some direct threats. Turn to 255.

97

You can place Dieter Francchi in London at the time of the bomb: he was the tourist who told Cohen to warn the police. You decide he is well worth finding out more about. Turn to 39.

98

You watch the comings and goings in the lane which ends at Jimbo's old farmhouse. Only two people go up the lane, and one of them is a postman. Then a van drives up to the house and through your binoculars you see that cases are being loaded on to the van by Jimbo, the van driver and the other person who went up the lane. What can you do to stop them getting away? Your own car will not block the road.

In the field close to the lane, you see a man using a digging machine to lay down pipes. You ask him if he will dig a large ditch across the lane to stop the van. It costs you £30, but with a mischievous grin the man starts to dig up the road. Meanwhile, you race off to the nearest phone and tell the Cambridge CID inspector that you suspect Jimbo is getting rid of his loot and what you have done to delay him. He laughs and says, 'Okay, T.S., I'll be along soon with a search warrant.' Turn to 142.

You find a patch of dense brush near by and secrete yourself thoroughly: what are a few scratches compared with the risk of being discovered? Dawn does not take long to arrive and is heralded by the sounds of cocks crowing, cows bawling and other signs of general activity, which show that people are waking up and starting a new day. You stay hidden all day, sleeping fitfully.

At dusk, you start back up the broken rock at the side of the avalanche scar, which gives you a perfect path nearly to the top of the mountain. You are thankful for the full moon, as long as it lasts. At the summit you bivouac for the night, out of sight of the valley below. You are starving, but you comfort your grumbling tummy with the thought that no one in ordinary circumstances has ever died through not eating for three days.

On the way down the other side the next day, you find the going moderately hard, but fun as well. You feel that something has been achieved, and not having to hide any more is a great relief. The first things you do when you get to the village at the foot of the mountain are eat, have a hot drink, bathe and change your clothes. Sometimes the simple things in life are definitely the best! Then you make arrangements for returning to London. Turn to **197**.

100

You may now investigate any of the following that you have not already investigated:

The explosive	Turn to **169**
The brown-paper bag	Turn to **118**
The timer	Turn to **23**
The clock	Turn to **13**
The teenager	Turn to **229**
Opportunity	Turn to **80**
Motive	Turn to **29**

101

Will you question the townspeople to find out who was responsible for your kidnapping (turn to **41**) or try to find some other line of investigation locally (turn to **264**)?

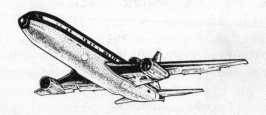

102

The report from the Essex police takes a few days to
arrive. In the meantime, you have been pursuing
other avenues. When the report arrives, it tells you
that two clocks of this type were sold by the
Harwich Woolworth's. However, the staff were
unable to identify, and therefore the police were
unable to locate, either customer. Mark *10* on the
Web. You can decide to go to Harwich yourself and
see if you can be more successful than the local
police (turn to **259**), or you can change to another
line of investigation (turn to **200**).

103

What about the motive of the crime, which was the
most complex thread to follow? If you have marked
on the Web *all* of *22, 55, 60, 3, 51, 20* and *50*, turn to
175. Otherwise, turn to **201**.

104

The Swiss are very annoyed at you for poking your nose into their security business, but Herr Galten, whom you met with Schwimmer, persuades the Swiss authorities not to take any action. He explains that you are just very persistent. Will you now investigate the missing bonds (turn to **164**) or the Hatton Garden robbery (turn to **2**)?

105

The Austrian factory manufactures explosives for both the government and private companies. One of their chief outlets is Switzerland, where there is a legal requirement that all new buildings must have nuclear fall-out shelters. The Austrian government also has a nuclear-shelter programme and uses explosives for blasting through rock to create deep enough shelters. Will you investigate the Austrian outlet (turn to **62**) or the Swiss outlet (turn to **15**)?

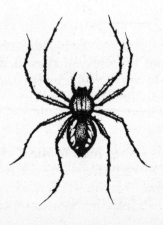

106

You stop drinking and regain a guard on your tongue. You try to steer the conversation around to topics of local interest. At one point you think of something Klaus said, and you ask the people near you in the bar who this 'spinner' or 'Spinne' is, remembering that *Spinne* is the German for 'spider'. The place falls quiet for an instant, but then jollity and noise resume. You notice someone nod to the others, leave the bar and walk outside. You see him through the window making for a telephone. Will you follow this person (turn to **155**), or sit tight and act as if nothing has happened (turn to **59**)?

107

James Cherkhom, when interviewed, states that he was indeed in the area at the time, but that he was having a cup of coffee while waiting to collect sandwiches for the office in which he works. While he was there, he heard the commotion caused by the discovery of the bomb and went out to see what it was all about.

You take the young man to the café to check his statement. The staff there verify that he was in the café at the time. You question the boy further, and find that he thinks he saw another messenger, whom he knows as Jerry, in the crowd around the Bank. He thinks that Jerry works for Loebs. Mark *15* on the Web and turn to **153**.

108

The Lion stays at the restaurant for another hour, and then abruptly gets up – as if at a signal, but you didn't see one – and leaves. The German agent stays to watch the others at the Lion's table. Will you follow the Lion (turn to **26**) or the man who left for Zurich (turn to **70**)?

109

Francchi came into Dover on the Calais–Dover ferry. You arrange for the French Immigration officials to check their records and report back to you. Their information suggests that Francchi arrived in Calais on the train from Amsterdam. This is surprising: surely it would have been quicker to have caught a ferry from Belgium or Holland, rather than travelling to Calais to do so. You try to pick up the trail in Amsterdam.

You have a friend in Interpol in Amsterdam, and he enables you to contact the relevant Dutch authorities. On the Continent, hotel records are carefully checked, so you are quickly on the scent. The Oranjeboom Hotel had Dieter Francchi staying for two nights; what is more, he coincided with another Swiss resident, whose name is given as Peter Klaus. If you have marked *32* on the Web, turn to **87**; otherwise, turn to **263**.

110

Things now become a lot clearer. Your instinct was right: it is not a fall-out shelter. When the avalanche hit, it must have destroyed the cave system where the famous Untersee cheese was finally shaped and left to mature. You know that the cheese-making enterprise is a cantonal business, so the fact that you got no help from Council officials or local people now makes sense. The whole thing must be an open secret in the area. But why do they not want anyone to know about it? It seems that they are trying to hide the disaster from the rest of the world. And what has all this got to do with the bomb in London? Turn to **171**.

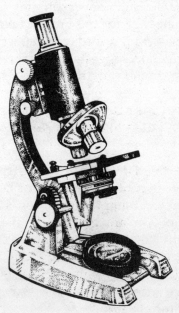

111

You arrange to be taken to Alicante in the police helicopter. You are enjoying the scenery below and are pleased not to have to drive all the way. Then the radio crackles into life and the pilot turns the helicopter inland and follows a road up into the mountains. There has been a terrorist attack: two policemen have been killed and all units have been alerted to be on the look-out for a particular car, which may be carrying the terrorists. Suddenly your pilot becomes excited and tells you that he has sighted the car. He flies low over it, and all at once the helicopter jolts as if struck by something: the occupants of the car are firing at you! The pilot shows you a rifle strapped to the side of the helicopter and asks if you can use it. You say you can. He holds the helicopter out of pistol range and you try to hit the car. It is very difficult, but after about ten shots you obviously hit a tyre. The car skids and piles into a tree. The helicopter hovers around until the local police arrive. There is a short gun battle, but eventually the gunmen are captured. However, the pilot now has to land at the local police head-quarters to give his report. The helicopter will not take off again until the next day. There are no cars available for hire, and you must wait. Turn to 158.

112

When goods are stolen, there is the problem of disposing of them at a reasonable price. This is a weak point in most crimes, and many thieves are caught through trying to sell the proceeds. But if a profit can be made someone will buy the goods off them and sell them as quickly as possible. Such people are known as fences and they tend to special-ize in different types of goods. Many crooks always use the same fence. In this case, you have a strong suspicion that a man known by his nickname of Jimbo will be the fence. You drive to his address and find a drinks party in full swing, with Jimbo's wife as the hostess, but no sign of Jimbo himself or any of his cronies. Will you stay to ask questions, hoping that drink may have loosened some tongues (turn to **231**), or will you leave and look for Jimbo (turn to **64**)?

113

Since all terrorists require publicity, occasionally they are willing to tell you things, provided that they do not implicate anyone who can be caught. Terrorists, in your experience, also like to boast about what they have done. So you decide to check up on terrorists, but you have contacts only with three groups. If you start with your Dutch connec-tions, turn to **145**; if you start with the German Baader–Meinhoff group, turn to **230**; if you start with Arab terrorists, turn to **262**.

114

John Colby has been a messenger with the Bank for ten years. He is a retired policeman and, as far as everyone in the Bank you speak to is concerned, is above suspicion. What about Colin Geary, a loan clerk? Turn to **222**.

115

The police take one look at your dishevelled appearance, listen to you going on about plots and kidnappers, and call in the doctor. He finds traces of barbiturate in your bloodstream, and the police dismiss your story as drug-induced illusions. You are sent home in disgrace, and Scotland Yard are quick to remove you from the case, before you stir up any more trouble.

116

After digesting the contents of the report on the road-building agency, you conclude that, while it might be possible to steal some of their explosives, anyone attempting to do so would be very foolish indeed, since it is an offence punishable by death, or at the very least a severe flogging. If you have not yet looked into the oil company, turn to **212**; if you have, turn to **268**.

117

In the morning, when you rise, he is not talkative; in fact, he seems rather sullen. You start off down the mountain, intending to cross the ridge into the next valley. You ask him innocent but leading questions, but he skilfully fences them all, and keeps asking you questions back about where you live and what sorts of things you write and so on. Turn to **149**.

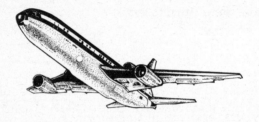

118

Expert examination of the bag shows it to be of continental manufacture: it measures about 24 by 18 inches, but the measurements are exact in metric terms. Further tests indicate that the paper from which the bag was made came from the area encompassing Germany, Austria and Switzerland, and that there is only one manufacturer of bags of this particular type. The factory is located in Austria. You find that the chief purchasers of these bags from the Austrians are in Denmark and Switzerland. Unfortunately, you also find that there is no way to distinguish one batch of bags from another, so that it is impossible to gain precise information about where your bag went. The design of the bag was changed four months ago, but that does not seem to be much help to you, since hundreds of thousands of them have been sold since then: they are used all the time on the Continent for carrying groceries. Will you leave the investigation into the bag there, so as not to spend time on inquiries which look set to get you nowhere (turn to **200**)? Or will you spend some more time and contact wholesalers of these bags in Denmark (turn to **239**) or Switzerland (turn to **277**)?

119

The tiny country of Liechtenstein, situated between Austria and Switzerland, used to make a good living from the manufacture of mechanical calculators. Although these are still in demand where batteries or electrical power are in short supply, the rise of the computer has killed Liechtenstein's industry in that area. So now it chiefly makes timers. The serial number of your timer shows that it was sold to Switzerland and ended up in a small canton called Untersee.

You get in touch with the Swiss police. They are very correct, but no police force likes terrorism or possible terrorism, and they all co-operate, even forces from some East European countries. The Swiss return the information almost immediately. The timer found its way to a workshop in the canton, where it was found to be defective and was discarded as useless. Turn to **146**.

120

You can trace precisely the type of plastic explosive used to Untersee. This is not very much in itself, but is good circumstantial evidence in conjunction with other evidence you have. You may also be able to show (if you have marked 13 on the Web) that the system used in Untersee for withdrawing explosives from the store is lax enough to allow someone who wanted to build up a secret hoard of the stuff to do so: this is more good circumstantial evidence.

The bag used to contain the bomb did not come up with anything concrete, but you can prove that bags of this type are sold in Switzerland, and the cheesy smell that minute analysis detected on the bag is corroboration, since Ulrich was transporting cheese in his lorry.

You have the shop assistant's evidence and the French police are still holding Ulrich for having bought the clock, which definitely ties him in with the crime. You are sure that further questioning, when Ulrich is faced with how much you know about the case, will make him break down and confess that he brought the explosive into the country as well, hidden somewhere in his lorry.

You can trace the timer to Untersee, and more specifically to the workshop in which Peter Klaus was employed. If you have further evidence about Klaus, you will be able to convict him. Turn to **14**.

121

As an experienced detective, you know that there are two main sorts of gain. There is *direct* gain, for instance in stealing money, or weapons, or jewellery, or anything that belongs to some other person; and there is *indirect* gain, for instance by causing a disturbance in one place to disguise the fact that a crime is being committed in another place. Do you think that the motive for the bomb was direct gain (turn to **54**) or indirect gain (turn to **79**)?

122

The police refuse to issue you a weapon. Will you look for other sources of weapons on the island (turn to **156**), or carry on the pursuit unarmed (turn to **71**), or return to London (turn to **202**)?

When you arrive at the chapel, Klaus looks very puzzled. 'There is a lock on the door,' he says. 'But there is never a lock on the door – never!' He seems almost angry. He gets tools from the balloon and cuts through the chain. You walk in and look around, with the help of torches, since it is now getting dark. You make out a plain chapel, with the benches pushed back against the walls and in the middle of the floor a tent, secured by ropes. 'What is this?' says Klaus. You tell him, with a calmness you do not feel, that you have heard of this before, and you suggest that he look inside the tent for a chair. He finds two chairs with handcuffs attached to them.

Now you are certain. 'This is a kidnappers' hide-out,' you explain. 'This is a method they use to keep the victim from being able to gain information about where they are.' What worries you, however, is that the tent has not been cleared away and the chapel was locked. It looks as though the kidnappers are planning to use it shortly.

You tell Klaus to run and fetch gas cylinders from the balloon. While he is away, you dismantle the tent and use it to make a sort of tunnel at the entrance to the chapel, so that anyone entering has to come through it. When Klaus returns, you poke the nozzles of two cylinders through the canvas and secure them with masking-tape.

Then you hear what you feared – sounds from

outside. You look through a chink and see in the moonlight two armed men. They are approaching cautiously, one well behind the other: it is probable that they saw your balloon coming down and have come to check on their hideout. You turn on the gas from one cylinder and fill the tent-tunnel with gas. You tell Klaus to stand by with the other cylinder. The door starts to open slowly: this must be the first kidnapper. Will you wait for the other one to come closer (turn to **76**) or take action now (turn to **11**)?

124

You and the ranger manage to make it down the mountain. Your bruises don't help, but he does know the easiest way down and where a phone can be reached. When you get to the phone, in the village café, you find two people who are obviously English. One of them is Gerald Cohen, the boy you have been looking for! Turn to **10**.

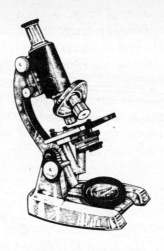

125

You dig around Liselle Goch's background. It turns out that, apart from being a director of Intercon, her main profession is banking, as Trencham had told you. She is in London at the moment, working for a small private bank, whose offices are directly opposite the Bank of England! The coincidences are too great. Perhaps you should look into what possible motive such a person could have for planting a bomb in the Bank of England (turn to **79**). Alternatively, if you have not completed your investigation of the explosive used, you could do so either by checking up on the manufacturers (turn to **261**) or by using your security contacts to pursue the possibility that the bomb was the work of terrorists (turn to **113**).

This fork leads to a large, slightly damp chamber with a marked cheesy smell; the walls are lined with racks. When you examine the racks, your first thought is, 'Some nuclear shelter this!' There are plenty of empty racks, but those that have anything in them are filled with large cheeses. It seems to you that no business would get fat on the sales of the few cheeses in this store, but perhaps there are others being ripened elsewhere. You know that some varieties of cheese are brought to special caves for the final stage of their manufacture.

You explore the extent of the chamber with your torch. Again, there is stonework in progress, just as there was in the main tunnel. At one end of the chamber are sliding doors, which on examination prove to be hydraulic and completely sealed against any air entering from outside. Your way out has to be the way you came in. You retrace your steps, thinking furiously about what you have seen. Turn to **256**.

127

The security forces are irritated with you. They may have appreciated your help in the past but you have no right to poke your nose into their affairs. They pull some official levers and strings and have you removed from the case.

128

You immediately start to collect all the relevant information about possible tourists. Because of Cohen's description, you know that the suspect is probably German, Austrian or Swiss. Collecting the information is a long and boring job, which is not reduced much by your decision to ignore all entrants into the country except those who gave Immigration an address in London. The information is available from the Home Office, backed up by the tour operators and hotel bookings. It takes three days to assemble the data, but the final table on your computer screen looks like this:

		AUSTRIAN VISITORS			GERMAN VISITORS			SWISS VISITORS		
Single	Females	12	30	10	15	14	6	10	6	3
Single	Males	8	5	5	12	11	9	5	3	2
Families	Females	3	8	2	5	20	1	1	3	6
Families	Males	1	7	0	0	8	2	0	2	0
Residents	Females	45	36	8	165	250	10	7	22	3
Residents	Males	60	40	20	200	150	50	36	20	5
Tourists	Females	21	7	8	13	11	22	9	1.	11
Tourists	Males	25	6	10	22	12	20	19	2	10
		under 20		over 60	under 20		over 60	under 20		over 60
Totals		175	139	63	432	476	120	87	59	40

Will you check on the Austrian visitors (turn to **60**), the German visitors (turn to **163**) or the Swiss visitors (turn to **73**)? Remember that you are looking for a male aged between twenty and sixty years old.

129

Another article catches your eye, from an issue of about six months ago:

> Miss Liselle Goch, chairwoman of the finance committee of the canton, announced today the resignation of the committee. She has been promoted by her bank to an important post in Italy. Herr Ulrich, owing to the nature of his occupation, is not able to carry out the increased load of work that will have to be done by the finance committee, and Herr Francchi, who is in charge of rebuilding, will need all his time for this task. Herr Peter Klaus has also moved house; he is now living in Basle and has become a mountain guide. Herr Spinne said that the extra work should be undertaken by a new committee and that wherever possible the old committee will help all they can. The Council of the canton proposed a vote of thanks to the retiring committee and a new committee was appointed.

The article goes on to give the names of the new committee, which are of no interest to you. Turn to **177**.

130

The Vulture has not been seen for some time. It is suspected that Israeli intelligence may have liquidated her. She was involved in the massacre of five children in Israel and there was eyewitness identification of her involvement. It is known that she was the object of a shoot-to-kill policy by Israeli intelligence. If you want to investigate the Lion, turn to 37; if you want to investigate the Eagle, turn to 22. If you have not done so already, you could look into Dutch terrorists (turn to 145) or German terrorists (turn to 230). If you have finished looking into the explosive and want to change tack altogether, turn to 200. Or you may still need to check up on the manufacturers of the explosive (turn to 261), or check whether the criminal underworld was the source (turn to 83).

131

The lorry was transporting a load of cheese to a warehouse in the Croydon area, just south of London. This looks hopeful. Further examination of the Customs log shows that the driver's name was Hans Ulrich, and that he was working for a distributor's in Zurich. Obviously you must go to the Croydon warehouse. You drive to Croydon via the Dartford Tunnel, having alerted the manager of the warehouse by phone that you are on your way and to stay late at work, if necessary, until you get there. He gives you a description of Ulrich as a roly-poly man with a moustache, so that fits with the shop-girl's description of the man who bought the clock.

Your next step is to ring up the Zurich distributor's. Turn to **32**.

You calculate that you have enough to make a visit to Untersee worth while. The picture is by no means complete, but pieces are starting to fall into place. Your encyclopedia gives you little information about Untersee. The town, the valley and the canton all share the same name. It is a small canton, or municipal district, of Switzerland, set in a mountain-fringed valley. Its chief sources of income are manganese and a particular variety of large-holed cheese.

If you have marked 32 on the Web, turn to **207**; if you have marked 33 on the Web, turn to **97**; if you have marked neither of these, turn to **28**; if you have marked both, turn to **181**.

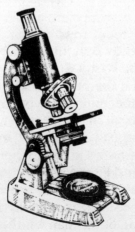

133

You charter a fast motor boat with radar; the radar makes the boat conspicuous, but without it you stand no chance. You think it unlikely that the villains will be heading north or west, since these directions lead to open sea. You use your radar to try to locate a boat which is not moving like a fishing boat, is fast, and is heading for the mainland. You pick up plenty of boats on the radar, but there is only one which fits the bill. It seems to be making for Lisbon in Portugal. You alert the Portuguese police by radio and brief them on the situation; it turns out that they have suspected for some time that a big-time dealer, specializing in international stolen goods, is based in Lisbon, though they have not yet been able to identify him or her. Your boat is considerably faster than that of the criminals, and you speed up to get to Lisbon ahead of them. Turn to **220**.

134

There are currently only three people on this file: one is in a mental hospital, so you can eliminate her straightaway. Of the other two, one now lives in Scotland and the other still lives in London. A telephone call is all that is needed to discover that the Scottish person was on holiday in Sweden at the time. The Londoner is a man who had started to drink too much. He had worked for the Bank for twelve years, but warnings made no difference and he just carried on drinking too much at lunch-times. He was sacked. This coincided with his wife leaving him and a car crash in which he broke his hip. He blames the Bank for all this. It takes time, but inquiries show that he has no expertise and no access to bomb-making equipment; you discard him as a possibility. Cross off 56 on the Web. If you want to look into the second part of the file, those who think that the Bank has been responsible for some personal misfortune of theirs, but who were not employees, turn to **154**. If you want to look into the third part, those who are convinced that the Bank is responsible for the ills of the world, turn to **226**. If you have finished with this line of inquiry and want to investigate another possible motive, turn to **29** and choose again.

135

The right-hand fork brings you to a large bay full of earth-moving equipment. In the back, behind the machinery, there is a sort of office. The door is not locked; you go in and start to search the place. In a large flat drawer you find what are obviously plans of the work to be done; in one corner of the office is a set of accounting books. You take pictures of both of these with your camera. Your training includes some knowledge of accounting and you settle down to see if you can make anything of the books. It immediately becomes clear that the work is on the canton's cheese-making facility, and you see that the work has a budget figure in Swiss francs roughly equal to £5 million. The work was started two years ago. Then something happened and it looks as though the work had to be started all over again: it dawns on you that the avalanche must have been responsible. Turn to 110.

136

You find that the lorries are still in the country, but are due to return today. You guess that they will travel back to Harwich along the M4, so you arrange for the motorway police to divert them to a service area and detain them. When you arrive at the service area, you find that the motorway police have just that moment led in the three lorries. It seems to both you and the police that the drivers are very worried, as if they had something to hide. You demand to see their tachograph – the instrument that keeps a record of the driver's speed, acceleration, time spent resting and so on. This worries them even more.

You examine the graph records and find that all three drivers seem to have covered more miles than they should have. The graph shows you that they took a detour and, by checking against a map, you can see when and where they did so. You judge that the detour would have taken them down to the Blackwater River. Armed with this information, you ask them for an account of their journey. Turn to **75**.

137

You ask him about the avalanche, but get nowhere. Instead, he turns a bit sullen and keeps asking you questions back, about where you live and what sorts of things you write and so on. Turn to **149**.

You use your computer network to get in touch with a friendly Soviet agent in Brussels. He knows nothing about the bomb, and assures you that his side had nothing to do with it. You ask him if he knows anything that might conceivably be useful – anything related to bombs or banks. The only thing he can tell you is that there is some activity going on in Swiss money circles. Nothing certain is known, but there is uneasiness in Geneva. You wonder what the possible connection could be with the case you are working on.

You make inquiries in Geneva on your own account, but there is no official interest and you wonder whether the unease, which you also detect, could be due to some gold transactions. If you think this is worth looking into, turn to **185**. If you think you should pry into what is going on in Swiss security, turn to **18**. Or will you go back to MI6 and Special Branch and demand to know what is going on in Switzerland (turn to **127**)?

139

It is beginning to look as though you are on the right trail. You start to trace back. Armed with Francchi's passport details, you contact Immigration Control, since Francchi is Swiss and Switzerland is not part of the EEC. You find eventually that he entered Britain at Dover; by checking the timing, you calculate that he must have got straight on to the London train, and gone from Victoria Station directly by taxi to the hotel. In other words, it would seem that he had no time to pick up anything extra, such as a bomb, which he would hardly have carried through Customs. Since you are sure that Francchi is a real suspect, it follows that someone else had the bomb; you now become certain that a conspiracy is involved. Turn to **109**.

You climb up into the barn, take off your wet clothes, lay them out in the sun, and lie down to wait. The heat, the buzz of flies and the general peaceful atmosphere soon send you off to sleep. You wake up with a start, wondering how long you have been asleep. Your next thought is to see whether or not your gear is dry.

To your astonishment, and then alarm, you cannot find your clothes. You get down from the barn, trying to cover yourself. This is very silly. What has happened? Have your clothes been stolen? But you know that in the Swiss valleys people leave their houses open: they do not bother to lock up, because no one steals.

You hear the noise of barking dogs. You worry that someone is coming: you do not want to be seen naked – in fact, you do not want to be seen at all! Then you see what has happened: a couple of puppies are playing with your clothes! You rush out at them. They are so surprised that they run away, yelping, and leave your stuff behind. You find that some of it is torn, but not much, and you are soon dressed – a little ragged and untidy, but dry, and ready to continue your journey. Mark 35 on the Web and turn to **203**.

141

You leave the ranger as comfortable as you can make him, and try to follow his instructions for getting down the mountain and to the nearest village. But the inevitable happens: a mist rises and you are not sure where you are. You cannot see where you are going, and darkness will soon be on you. You decide at least to keep heading down. Then you see the flicker of a campfire further up the hill, to your right. At the same time, you have begun to see the lights of what may be a village lower down the mountain. Will you make for the campfire (turn to **234**) or the village (turn to **276**)?

142

While you are waiting for the police to arrive, the van starts to leave, but is unable to pass the trench. The driver gets out of the van and looks around nervously. Then he goes back to the house and you see him talking to Jimbo. They unload the van. At last the police arrive with a search warrant. They detain Jimbo and the other two and proceed to search the house. But after two hours the cases still have not been found. You have an idea and you look carefully at the outside of the house. Sure enough, the shape of the outside wall of the dining-room does not coincide with the interior layout. You point this out to the police and before long they have broken into the priest's hole. Inside they find a treasure-house of precious goods – including the stolen Hatton Garden jewellery. Turn to **248**.

143

Spinne came to England by the Dutch KLM airline from, you assume, Amsterdam. Again, when you check the method of payment, you find that his journey was paid for by the German bank. At the duty-free shop it is the same story. It transpires that Lufthansa flew Spinne into Amsterdam from Frankfurt. There were no problems with luggage and so on or passport. He arrived only ten minutes before take-off, but had arranged to be met and rushed through the formalities. You try to find out the reason for the lateness of his arrival.

You find that he arrived at Frankfurt by helicopter. The helicopter was registered in Zurich. You ask for a copy of the flight plan and discover that Spinne had the helicopter and the pilot for the previous two days as well, and that thirty-six hours before he went to Amsterdam the helicopter had taken him to Germany, to the town of Limburg, which is near Frankfurt. Payment for the helicopter had as usual been made through the bank. Mark 50 on the Web. Obviously, you had better get on to this bank. Turn to **249**.

144

Scotland Yard issues an urgent request to see you at once. You go there and are ushered into one of the most unpleasant interviews of your life. Chief Superintendent Boyson is implacable. After much argument, he concludes, 'I'm sorry, T.S., but there it is. The powers that be feel that you are spending too much time on this case for too few results. As of now, you're off the case.'

145

Your contacts in Holland are the sort who, while not knowing details, can tell you if particular groups are likely to be involved in specific revolutionary action. You let them know that you would like information on Dutch-based terrorists and whether they seem to have any interest in the Bank bomb. The answer is, 'No, T.S., but please would you let us know if you find out anything.' Will you next look into the Baader–Meinhoff gang (turn to **230**) or Arab terrorists (turn to **262**)? Or, if you have finished investigating terrorists, will you get in touch with your underground informants to see if the bomb was the work of British criminals (turn to **83**), or will you check up on the manufacturers of the explosive (turn to **261**)? If you have finished looking into the explosive and want to change tack altogether, turn to **200**.

146

Since the timer was used as an integral part of the bomb and was far from useless, all the three people employed in the workshop fall under suspicion. They are Albert Schmidt, a quiet married man with three children; Heinrich Popper, a loud-mouthed socialist and a highly skilled engineer; and Peter Klaus, a quiet unmarried man with a record of civic service. Will you ask for further information on Schmidt (turn to 270), Popper (turn to 90) or Klaus (turn to 186)?

147

You think about what you know, and the more you think about it, the more the mystery seems to centre on the avalanche and the cheese. However, you do not fancy your chances of being freely admitted to the site where, it is claimed, the repairs to the avalanche damage are going on and nuclear shelters are being built, so you reckon there is only one thing to be done: you must try to get into it without anyone knowing. Approaching the site from Untersee itself would be too obvious and public, but you look at a map and you think that it might be possible if you come over the mountain from the other side. You will have to arrange the timing so that it is dusk when you arrive, when the children are bringing the animals down from the mountain pastures, and people will be looking forward to their suppers, not up at the mountains. You drive over to the other side of the mountain and hire some camping gear in a small village. Turn to 194.

148

The Deuxième Bureau tells you what you already know, that getting real information out of Libya is very difficult. However, they do have good relations in such matters with an Italian specialist who does business with the country. His family is influential there, and such ties are very important in Libya. He promises to do what he can. You have to wait for seven days for the information, during which time you explore other avenues. When the report comes, the two main users of this type of explosive in Libya turn out to be an oil company, which is part American and run very tightly indeed, and the government road-building agency, which is not so businesslike, despite the fact that the government maintains strong control over all matters likely to be dangerous, such as using explosives. If you want to discover what the report has to say on the oil company, turn to 212; if you want to read its conclusions about the road-building agency, turn to 116.

149

You reach a ridge, where you rest. You take off your rucksack and rest it on a rock. Then you move into the attack yourself. 'Why do you ask me all these questions?' you ask. 'Do you ask all your clients such details? Something is bothering you about me: what is it?' He makes an impatient gesture and nudges your rucksack by mistake, and it falls over the edge of the small cliff on top of which you are sitting.

Klaus apologizes, leaves his gear with you, and goes down to collect your rucksack. He gets down okay, but the climb back is more difficult. He has your rucksack on his back, for one thing; but he is still preoccupied and is not really watching what he is doing. He stumbles against a rock and twists round: the rucksack catches on a rough edge. He loses his footing and his grip and falls about fifteen feet down the rock-strewn slope. When he comes to a rest, he lies still. You climb down to him and he looks at you. 'Vigilance is the price,' he says, trying to smile. 'The mountains have no mercy.' His last words sound like 'Tell it to the spinner'; then he faints with pain. You try to find out what his injuries are, but you do not move him and can see nothing obvious. You stick a pencil between his teeth and wonder what to do next. Then you spot a small collection of buildings not too far away down the mountainside. Turn to **162**.

150

The police have been putting together for you a report containing details of other crimes that were committed near by at roughly the same time as the bomb scare and on the same day. You find that there are two crimes or alleged crimes which seem to fit; and there is one further incident, which you don't know how to classify – as a crime or what. The two possible crimes are the loss of bonds worth £8 million from a private bank across the road from the Bank of England and the armed robbery of a Hatton Garden jewellers. The other incident is that several witnesses reported seeing a Securicor van behaving peculiarly on Threadneedle Street at the time: it kept changing lanes and weaving in and out of the busy rush-hour traffic. Will you look into the missing bonds (turn to **164**), the jewellery robbery (turn to **2**) or the Securicor van (turn to **242**)?

151

You go to Bristol. Kosinski is part of the Polish community, who tend to be very defensive and to give no information to strangers. But you find out that he frequents a particular snooker club when he is in town. You gain entrance to the club. Neither Kosinski nor Penny is around, but you learn that they were there, but have left, apparently to go on holiday together. It does not take too long to find out that their destination is Madeira. You wonder whether they have taken the loot with them or have already disposed of it. Turn to **172**.

152

The Council is, if anything, even more obstructive: they simply refer you to a resolution of a Council meeting at which it was recommended that work be started at the avalanche site, as per an earlier resolution. This is not very informative, and just leads to more paperwork. You wade through all the past Council minutes and eventually find the resolution you are looking for. It says that work on a Council or civic fall-out shelter should be started as soon as adequate financial means are found. No reason is given, but there is a reference to the previous meeting of the Council. You go back to the minutes of this meeting and find that both Dieter and Peter Klaus had been on the Council at the time. Very interesting, and another connection between these two. You think that you had better have a look at this fall-out shelter some time. You cannot see what connection there could possibly be with your case, but the coincidence is a bit much. Will you go to the works site now (turn to **78**), or will you first try to find out more about Peter Klaus (turn to **24**)?

153

You go to Peabody, King and Loeb with the youth's description and find that it perfectly matches Gerald Cohen. However, you do not find this as a result of meeting Cohen face to face: he has just gone on holiday to Spain with his brother, and is not due back for another twelve days. You use the computer to trace him, and find that he and his brother left from Stansted airport. A check with Spanish Customs shows that the Cohens are booked into a hotel in Barcelona. You know that you cannot afford to wait until they return, and since Gerald is potentially your only reliable witness, or may even be implicated in the crime, you decide that it is worth travelling to Spain to see him. Turn to **198**.

154

There are currently fifty names on this file. It would take a lot of time to check up on all of them thoroughly, so you decide to adopt some criterion for elimination. You discard all those who write regularly, or have done so in the very recent past, because you think that anyone intending to set a bomb would not draw attention to themselves. This narrows the list down to two names. Both the writers say little more than, 'You have ruined me, damn you!'

One turns out to be a harmless old lady of fifty-five who really would not hurt a fly; by the end of your phone call with her, you are not at all sure what injury she imagined the Bank to have done her. The other is a vicar who had invested in currency funds, and because he did not understand currency changes he thought that the Bank had deliberately swindled him when he lost most of his money. You cannot bring yourself to believe that a vicar would plant a bomb. If you want to look into the first part of the file, consisting of former employees of the Bank who blame the Bank for their misfortunes, turn to **134**. If you want to look into the third part of the file, those who are convinced that the Bank is responsible for the ills of the world, turn to **226**. If you have finished with this line of inquiry and want to investigate another possible motive, turn to **29** and choose again.

155

As you walk out of the door, you feel a needle being jabbed into your thigh . . . and then you remember nothing coherent. You have the vague impression that you are put on a stretcher, and you seem to hear the sound of a motor, but it all fades out. Turn to **219**.

156

You do eventually track down a shady, wealthy merchant, whose chief source of income seems to be gun-running. But the local police have been following you. They arrest you (but, to your surprise, do nothing about the gun-runner) and send you home in disgrace. Scotland Yard cannot afford to displease their counterparts even in a small island like Madeira, and you are promptly taken off the case.

You find the Swiss security forces, whom you get in touch with, strangely uncooperative on the topic of Herr Schwimmer. In fact, you detect an air of embarrassment. It seems to you that you are getting the run-around and you use your political contacts to get to the higher officials. Eventually, you are invited to see the man in charge. When you enter the office of this Herr Galten, you realize why you met with such reluctance to say anything. Sitting in the office is Herr Schwimmer! Luckily they trust you. They tell you that he is an undercover operative of the Swiss security forces and is, in fact, their main link between Hamburg and Zurich terrorists, whose groups he has infiltrated. No wonder the Swiss are so effective at preventing terrorism!

You talk to Schwimmer and explain why you were in Hamburg and interested in the Lion. He does not know anything about any explosive being supplied and is convinced that the Lion is lying low at the moment. All three of you discuss your problem, and the Swiss promise you any help they can give you, 'within Swiss law, of course', should you need it. You return to London. Mark *40* on the Web. You may now investigate any of the following you have not already looked into: the Eagle (turn to **22**), the Vulture (turn to **130**), Dutch terrorist groups (turn to **145**) or the Baader–Meinhoff gang (turn to **230**). If you have finished exploring the possibility that there is some terrorist connection to the bomb at the Bank of England, you can get in touch with your criminal underworld informants (turn to **83**) or the manufacturers of the explosive (turn to **261**). If you have finished looking into the explosive and want to change tack altogether, turn to **200**.

158
It is mid-morning by the time you arrive at the hotel where the Cohens are staying – only to find that Gerald has already left with his brother to go climbing in the nearby mountains. Will you wait for them to return (turn to **204**) or follow them (turn to **190**)?

159
The agents have no information which can help you. Will you now investigate the Hatton Garden robbery (turn to **2**) or the missing bonds (turn to **164**)?

160
When you get there, you find the villa empty and showing signs of having been hastily abandoned. That was a fruitless trip. Now you face an even longer trek back to Funchal. Mark 47 on the Web and turn to **257**.

161
You already know that Klaus and Francchi, whom you strongly suspect, are associates. You cannot find out more about Klaus without actually going to Untersee. Mark 32 on the Web and turn to **200**.

162

You make your way down. On the way you are met
by a boy who is leading a big man. It turns out that
the boy was out looking for a lost sheep and saw
what happened; he ran to a farm and the farmer
alerted the rescue team, which is already on its way.
The farmer has a first-aid kit with him.

Within twenty minutes, a group of six men come up
the side of the mountain with that slow, rolling gait
that eats up the distances. Their breathing is hardly
disturbed, despite all the emergency equipment
they are bringing with them. One of them is a
doctor. You had heard that mountain rescue teams
were efficient, and now you know it. They strap
Peter Klaus on to a stretcher and set off down
the mountain to the nearest small hospital. You
follow at a more leisurely pace, and check that
Klaus is comfortable. The doctor tells you that
he has a cracked pelvis, which would have been
made much worse if you had tried to move him.
You reflect that, if you can solve the case in the
next few days, you will at least know where Klaus
is. Turn to **52**.

163

In the list of single male visitors, you start with
eleven German possibilities. You eliminate those
with beards or moustaches, those over six foot, and
those who are very thin. This leaves you with only
one person and further checking reveals that he was
nowhere near London at the time. All this work is

very boring, but then police work often is. You continue your routine checking.

There are 150 recent entrants on residents' visas and it takes quite a long time to cut the list down to reasonable proportions. However, over one hundred of them are employed in consular or diplomatic duties and can be checked quickly with the co-operation of the Germans themselves, with whom you have an excellent working relationship. The rest, after the usual elimination procedures, can be reduced to five possibles. Two of these are friends and were away in Birmingham together; one is newly wed and on his honeymoon; and the other two cannot be traced for interview at the moment.

The eight men on the list of family groups are eliminated very quickly. It turns out, by some strange coincidence, that those who are not bearded or moustached are all in the 20–25 age-group and so are too young to resemble the suspect.

There are twelve in the category of Germans in tourist parties, eight with one package holiday, four with another. Checking with the couriers, who have to look up their records, reveals that none was missing from either party at the relevant time.

Mark 11 on the Web. If you now want to check up on Swiss visitors, turn to 73; if you want to look into Austrian visitors, turn to 60. If you want to spend more time pursuing the two missing German residents, turn to 17. If you have had enough of checking up on visitors, turn to 200.

164

Bearer bonds are promises to pay whoever has the bonds on a particular date the full sum mentioned at the place mentioned. Since no names are specified except those of the debtors, they are highly negotiable: *whoever* has the bonds on the due date can claim from the debtors. But they are very rarely stolen, because how could the thieves claim? As soon as they turned up on the due date with the bonds, they would be arrested; or, if they had already sold them to someone else, the bonds could still be traced back to them. There are two possibilities as regards the missing bonds. If you think it unlikely that they have been stolen, then they must have simply gone astray (turn to 258). If you think that they have been stolen, a more time-consuming task faces you: you must interrogate all the suspects in the bank and trace the history of the bonds. If you think that this avenue is worth this much time, turn to 208.

165

The six lorries from Holland had three different destinations: three went to Bristol, two to Birmingham and one to Romford. You quickly eliminate the

Birmingham and Romford lorries: their arrival times show that they made no detours on the way to their destinations, and all of them were reloaded and returned to Holland on the next available ferry. But the Bristol lorries are a different matter. There was certainly time for any of them to have entered London on the way to Bristol. In fact, since regulations require at least two stops during such a journey, it would have been easy. You check with their destinations and with the Customs computer. If you have marked three or fewer numbers on the Web, turn to **136**; if you have marked more than three, turn to **254**.

A criminal might bring pressure to bear on a victim by implied or actual threats. For instance, if a shop-keeper walked into his shop one morning and found paraffin-soaked rags all over the place, the *implied* threat is, 'We can burn you at any time, if we want to.' Telling the shopkeeper directly and specifically 'You do this and that, or else . . .' would be an *actual* threat. Will you look into the possibility that the bank has received implied threats (turn to **96**) or actual threats (turn to **255**)?

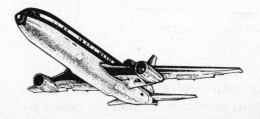

167

The police arrive in force and arrest everyone in sight, including you. Joe the Bunce has done a vanishing trick. You try to show the police your papers, but they refuse to look at them and you and everyone else are taken to Tottenham Court Road police station. At long last it is your turn to be interviewed, but you refuse until you have seen a senior officer. When he arrives, you show him your papers and explain what you were doing and what actually happened. The police apologize and release you, but the inspector suggests that next time you let some responsible person know your movements.

While you were waiting to be interviewed, you were pondering the tale you happened to overhear about the lady banker: after all, banking is what you are currently involved with. Should you look into this? If you have marked 55 on the Web, you decide not to; but if you have not marked 55 on the Web, you may look into the matter which so amused the Hooray Henrys by turning to **4**. Otherwise, you can check up on the manufacturers of the explosive (turn to **261**) or use your security contacts to investigate the possibility that the bomb was planted or supplied by terrorists (turn to **113**). Alternatively, you could change tack altogether (turn to **200**).

168

You land fairly close to Untersee. Klaus is apologetic about your curtailed holiday, and says, 'But, as my friend Spinne says, what can we do about the forces of nature?' There is a catch in his voice when he says this. However, you are glad that you decided to land, because the wind is really strong now. The next moment, the forces of nature catch up with Klaus: a sudden gust snaps the moorings of the balloon and hurls it against him. He lies on the ground in pain, and you think he may have broken a leg. You run into town for help and return with a doctor and a stretcher party. With mixed feelings you watch them take Klaus off to hospital: at least his movements will be hampered, should you want to arrest him in a hurry! Turn to **52**.

169

You wait for the experts' report on the explosive. You spend the time reading up on plastic explosives and find that there are two main illegal sources – industries such as mining, and the armed forces. Statistics show that, by and large, ordinary criminals get theirs from industrial sources, while terrorists get theirs from either source, depending on whether they are being supplied by sympathetic or unscrupulous individuals or governments.

You receive the scientific report on the explosive. It was approximately five pounds in weight and would have blown a four-foot hole in the wall of the Bank. The timer would have triggered an electrical spark, which would have detonated the explosive. The bomb was simple, but effective: the person who assembled it knew what he or she was doing.

Since each manufacturer uses slightly different ingredients, the explosive can be traced. The company which made it has three plants, one in Britain, one in Austria and one in France. Will you check up on these manufacturers (turn to **261**), will you use your underworld informants to investigate possible criminal involvement in the bomb (turn to **83**), or will you use your security contacts to investigate terrorists (turn to **113**)?

170
You key into the police computer and collate all information that might be relevant to your case. Among the items is one that relates to a rumour, overheard in a night club by a certain Joe the Bunce – a crook who occasionally acts as a police informer – that a lady banker was seen wearing overalls on the day of the bomb scare. If you have crossed off 55 on the Web, turn to **200**; otherwise, turn to **4**.

171
Exploration has taken you quite a time. It is now past midnight. You explore some of the tunnels which are being excavated to house the maturing

cheeses, and make a note of which ones end after only a short distance, and which ones tend upwards or go further into the mountainside. There is a sudden noise of feet, making no attempt to be quiet. You switch off your torch and take cover inside one of the tunnels which go further into the mountain. This is just as well, since the place is suddenly ablaze with light. You peek around the corner and see Peter Klaus come into the chamber: he is on crutches. Someone else is following him, but you do not have time to see who it is; you only know when you hear Klaus address his companion as 'my dear Dieter'. Turn to **215**.

172

Further inquiries reveal that all the three members of the gang have rented a villa together on Madeira. The booking was made some time ago, so it looks as though the robbery was planned well in advance. Mark 64 on the Web. You could follow them to the island (turn to **27**), or, if you think that the loot has already been passed on, you could try to trace the fence (turn to **112**). Alternatively, you could end this line of inquiry and investigate either the Securicor van (turn to **242**) or the missing bonds (turn to **164**), or change tack altogether (turn to **200**).

Klaus responds with remarks about the beauty, and says that some day ballooning will be even better, because the burners will not be so noisy. It is true that the noise interrupts conversation and distracts your attention from the view, because from time to time the burners ignite with a roar, to heat up the air in the balloon. You ask about the weather forecast, and he says that it is fair, but there is an area of high pressure developing over Czechoslovakia, which might move quite rapidly to the south-west.

Sure enough, the journey shortly becomes pretty bumpy, and you are beginning to hit areas of turbulence. Then the wind starts to blow fairly strongly, and Klaus begins to look worried. He says that you have a choice: either you can land as soon as possible or you can go with the wind, which would be exciting, but could be dangerous. If you decide to land, turn to **168**; if you run before the wind, turn to **235**.

174

You go to the restaurant car together, where you have breakfast. Talk turns to fraud and money, and in particular computer frauds involving breaking into banks' computers. You try to get him to talk about terrorism, but he returns to the subject of fraud. As you actually know quite a lot about this, you change the subject and try to talk about Switzerland. You are still talking about Switzerland when you return to your compartment; the conversation and a nap take up the rest of the time to Zurich. You reflect on the subject of fraud and wonder whether this could provide a motive for the Bank bomb. Will you return to London and try to discover the motive for the crime (turn to 29), or will you continue your interest in terrorism by tracking the mysterious Herr Schwimmer (turn to 157)?

175

Up until two years ago, Untersee had a flourishing cheese-making facility. The canton co-operative decided to extend the facility. In order to do so, they raised a loan secured by bearer bonds. Work was progressing well – but then disaster struck. An avalanche wiped it out. If this had just damaged the extension work, things might not have got out of hand; but the avalanche had a side-effect, which appeared only a few months later: the delicate atmosphere in the caves where the cheeses were matured had been altered, so that they were no longer suitable for making the distinctive and world-famous Untersee cheeses.

In one stroke, the valley's livelihood was ruined. They could not claim on insurance, or make the accident public at all, because once word got out that Untersee cheeses would be off the market for a while their customers would go elsewhere for reliable supplies. The best the canton could do was keep a trickle of cheeses going, while promising more 'once the extension is completed'. Nor could they raise another loan, as they now had no security. There was still plenty of money left from the loan: they worked furiously on rebuilding, under the guise of excavating a nuclear fall-out shelter for the community.

The members of the canton's finance committee put their heads together. The plan was probably formulated by the Spider, but you cannot prove it. When they were ready for action, they resigned all at once. Liselle Goch, who is a brilliant banker, used her position to gather the majority of the bonds into one place. This took the best part of six months. When she was ready, she sent word and instructions about the timing.

You know that Spinne was near Frankfurt, and that Klaus and Franchi were also there: you suspect that they met to make the final arrangements. They went to London. The bomb was assembled and placed, and warning was given. While Goch's colleagues in her banking office were looking out of the window, she coolly removed the parcel of bonds, including most of Untersee's, and shredded them. In her capacity as director of the cleaning company Intercon, she returned to the office that evening and made sure that the shredded documents were burned.

Were it not for your skill as a detective, T.S., the plan would have worked: no bearer bonds means no payment due, and Untersee would have been able to refurbish and extend their cheese-making facility, having effectively stolen nearly £5 million. You feel ambivalent – the cause was good, but the means were criminal. As a result of your investigations, you have enough evidence to extradite and convict Goch, Ulrich, Klaus and Francchi. The Spider, however, remains at large. Perhaps he is spinning another web for you even now . . .

176

You get on the phone to your friend in MI6 and arrange to meet her for lunch. She tells you that she will see if the matter is under heavy wraps, in which case she will be able to tell you nothing; if not, she will tell you what she can. You enjoy lunch and off she goes. She rings you back that evening and says, 'T.S., I've asked around and the word is that there is no great secret involved, just a bit of mopping up.' She goes on to say that there is a cast-iron guarantee that there could be no connection at all between their work and the bomb at the Bank of England. Mark 52 on the Web.

You accept that there is no connection between the bomb scare and MI6 operations, but you think that it might be as well to clear up whether the Soviets were involved, or know anything. They usually co-operate if the event is not political, and sometimes even when it is. Your friend also suggests that you might contact them, because they were as interested as MI6 in who might have been involved in the bomb, and perhaps they have different sources of information from MI6. Turn to **138**.

177

You read through this issue with increased interest. On the second page is an article which you had previously overlooked:

It is with great regret that this paper announces the retirement of one of the most respected citizens of our canton, Herr Wolf Spinne. Herr Spinne was born into the locally well-known family in March 1926 and was educated at the Gymnasium in Geneva. His education was interrupted during the early 1940s for reasons which we in this district know well. His exploits as a youngster, leading groups out of the dangers of the Third Reich, are legends to us all, as are his activities with the Red Cross in connection with the troubles in Hungary in his thirtieth year.

But all this is by the way. He has proved many times to us all that he is prepared to devote time and trouble and labour to help the people of our canton.

Herr Spinne married his wife, Gisela, in 1947, and after graduating with honours in Philosophy in Geneva he returned to us in Untersee and went to work in his father's business. In time he took over the business, and his son Wilhelm, thirty-four, now takes over in his place. Herr Spinne now has four grandchildren and, as he says, 'My wife and I will be able to be free to visit my family more often.' His unceasing work will be sorely missed by us all.

Turn to **46**.

178

Will you now investigate the Dutch lorries (turn to **165**), the Austrian lorries (turn to **244**) or the Swiss lorry (turn to **131**)?

179

The report goes into the Eagle's immediate past. He has had very strong contacts with E T A, the Basque separatist movement in Spain, and with the Corsican independence movement; and at one time he was deeply involved with I R A activities, but he lost patience with them as 'political babies'. During the last year he is known to have been in Uruguay, perhaps for a meeting with the Jackal, in January; in February he was in Athens, probably planning the Corsican bomb outrage which killed a French senator. From March to May he was in England, taking no known action. In June he disappeared from view, only to reappear in Cambridge at the end of

July. There is no proof, but he may have been involved in an Italian kidnapping during this period. Turn to **251**.

180

You devise a computer program based on the fact that the new-formula explosive has been in production for only the past year, and looking for either regular orders or orders shortly before the bomb scare. Excluding all semi-government agencies and all private individuals, you come up with three possibilities: public works in the canton of Pitterbach, which were contracted out to a private company; geological alterations undertaken by a private contractor in the canton of Krefelburg for the building of a new residence; and work in the canton of Untersee, where both the extraction of manganese and the construction of a civic nuclear fall-out shelter are requiring explosives. You add this information to your dossier: mark 42 on the Web. If you have not already done so, will you check up on the French explosives factory (turn to **9**)? You might still want to explore the possibility that the explosive was supplied by either terrorists (turn to **113**) or criminals (turn to **83**). Alternatively, if you have finished investigating the explosive, turn to **200**.

181

You can place Dieter Francchi in London at the time of the bomb: he was the tourist who told Cohen to warn the police. You know that Dieter and Peter Klaus were together in Amsterdam and Frankfurt.

You are certain that Klaus supplied the timer for the bomb and, given his mechanical expertise, you are pretty sure that he was the one who assembled the bomb. You cannot place him in London at the time, but maybe he sneaked into the country, or maybe he did not register with British Immigration as visiting London: you have checked only the London visitors. You decide to do a little more checking on Francchi, and then to concentrate on the more elusive Klaus. Turn to **39**.

182

Clearly Ms Goch is up to her neck and beyond in this business, and when you discover that she was the chief negotiator in Hessemann and Pinelli when the loan came up, you are sure that you have enough to convict her of something. At the very least, since you know that she comes from the canton of Untersee, she should have declared an interest when the matter of the loan was first broached and is guilty of dubious banking practice. But when you return from your office, where you were ringing Switzerland, to the private bank, you find that Goch has disappeared: your persistent questioning of her colleagues must have scared her. You go back to your office again, feeling somewhat despondent. Mark 22 on the Web and turn to **170**.

183

Will you try to get into the works site where you were refused entrance (turn to **243**) or try some other line of investigation locally (turn to **264**)?

184

You decide to try out an Italian *autostrada*, so you hire a powerful car. You hold the speed down until you reach the open road at Bologna, and then you have the exhilarating experience of travelling at 120 m.p.h. until you reach Piacenza. From Piacenza to Milan is a much slower road, but you feel sure that you have reached Milan before Ulrich. But the frustration of Florence is repeated in Milan. When you get to the place where Ulrich is expected, you are told that he rang to change the order of his delivery: he is going first to Nice in France and will only return to Milan in three or four days. Again it occurs to you to give up this wild-goose chase. If you do so, turn to **6**. Otherwise, turn to **38** to continue the pursuit to Nice.

185

You check with your connections in the bullion business, but this is a dead end. The only worry at the moment among some dealers is how much gold is going to be recovered by a salvage crew, who have discovered a treasure-ship sunk during the Second World War. Will you now investigate the Hatton Garden robbery (turn to **2**) or the missing bonds (turn to **164**)?

186

Peter Klaus is a qualified engineer; he is very clever with his hands. He has served as a local councillor, and his reserve army rank is that of a major. Bearing in mind his age, which is thirty, this is accelerated promotion. Obviously, he is a very able man. All the information you can get on him is, you are not surprised to see, very favourable. You wonder why he is no longer a councillor, since you read that he resigned and did not stand for election again. After his stint in local politics, he left his job in the workshop and became a tourist guide, based in Basle. Further inquiries show that during the three days preceding the bomb scare he was not seen anywhere. Of course, he *may* just have been out as a guide somewhere. If you have marked 33 on the Web, turn to **161**. Otherwise, if you want to hear about Schmidt, turn to **270**, and if you want to hear about Popper, turn to **90**. If you have finished reading the report on all three, mark 32 on the Web and turn to **200**.

187

There are times in every detective's career when he or she knows who the guilty party is, but is unable to produce enough evidence to secure conviction. It is partly for such cases that legal systems like those of Scotland have the dangerous, but useful, intermediate area between plain guilty or innocent – guilty, but not proven.

You know that the Spider helps those who seem to have a moral case for requiring assistance. It looks as though he is provided with funds for doing this, and that he does not take advantage of these funds and spend any of the money on himself. When he is a shoemaker, he lives like a shoemaker; but when he is a philanthropist, he spends as necessary. But it is his very philanthropy that convinces you that he is not just involved in the bomb scare, but even masterminded the whole affair: now that you know more about him, you can see that it bears his hallmarks. You have to accept, however, that you do not have enough evidence to warrant extradition or to bring him to trial.

Meanwhile, the British authorities have been reviewing the case. How much evidence have you provided them with? Turn to **81**.

188

Although Maerling's politics are fairly extreme, inquiries at the British Library show that he is diligent in his work. He is usually waiting to enter when the Library is opened in the morning and was certainly working there on the morning of the bomb, because his name is down for withdrawing books then. Will you now check up on Francchi (turn to **40**) or Pauli (turn to **51**)? Alternatively, you could return to **73** to choose another category of Swiss visitor to look into or, if you haven't already done so, check up on Austrian (turn to **60**) or German (turn to **163**) visitors. If you have had enough of checking up on tourists, turn to **200**.

189

You sip the drink . . . and you remember nothing more. You have a feeling that you are put on a stretcher, and you seem to hear the sound of a motor, but it all fades out. Turn to **219**.

190

You drive to the town of Alcoy and arrive at about 1 p.m. Nobody is around: the place seems to be deserted. You have arrived at the time of siesta, and it is nearly four o'clock before you find out that the brothers were seen to drive up into the national park area and are probably camping out somewhere in the huge park. It is late at night when you reach the park headquarters, and nothing can be done until the next day. You think wryly to yourself that at this rate you might as well have waited in London for Cohen to return from holiday: at least you could have been getting on with something else. Turn to **95**.

191

You have been fired at by dangerous criminals with an Uzi machine-pistol. Will you go to the local police with a request for firearms (turn to 122) or carry on with your pursuit unarmed (turn to 71)?

192

You move towards the draught that you felt earlier. You come across a patch of light, like a crack between rocks. It is very faint, so the crack cannot be very big and perhaps they do not know of its existence. You dare not use your torch to give yourself a better view. You notice that you can see more stars higher up the crack than lower down: it is wider up there, but it still does not look wide enough to squeeze through. You scramble up anyway, and find that it is wider than you thought: the reason you could not see more stars is that the entrance is covered by a shrub! At last you are out in the open air! Mark 20 on the Web. Turn to 99.

193

This takes time. The relevant pallets have to be found in the stores' warehouses, and some of these little branches are not yet computerized. Then the boxes have to be opened, to check that all the clocks they ordered are present and correct. In the end you discover that your clock did go to the Harwich branch after all. Mark 46 on the Web. Will you go to Harwich yourself (turn to 259), or will you put the matter in the hands of the local Essex police (turn to 102)?

194

You check into the hotel for the night, and are ready the next morning as soon as you have finished an early and hearty breakfast. The mountain is pretty high, and although there is no serious climbing to be done, accidents can happen. You set out at a slow, steady pace. It is a beautiful day and you are moving up the mountainside just as the goats and sheep are being taken out to pasture. There are even cattle on the way, because the mountain is dotted with little meadows, which are not much bigger than aprons, from your point of view. Some are steep, but some are like little tables built out from the side of the mountain to make more space. You check your map and start moving up to higher levels. During the long winter, all this would be under snow; but, once the ice has melted, the grass grows fast and the wild flowers spring up, bloom and seed as though they knew how short a season they have. Turn to **260**.

195

However, this was all some time ago, and you are informed that you can no longer meet either the security agents or the terrorists involved. Will you now investigate the Hatton Garden robbery (turn to **2**) or the missing bonds (turn to **164**)? Alternatively, you could get in touch with the Soviets to find out if they have any interest in or knowledge of the bomb (turn to **138**).

196

You put a banking accountant on to the job of

tracing the complete history of the bonds. When his report comes, you are fascinated to read that Liselle Goch was the chief negotiator on behalf of Hessemann and Pinelli when they were approached by Untersee about a loan. Since she comes from Untersee, she should at the very least have declared an interest and ruled herself out of negotiating. She is clearly guilty of dubious banking practice – but you suspect she may be guilty of more than that.

The report continues that, in the author's opinion, the bonds were deliberately gathered together by a banker of great skill. He cannot give you a name, but he suspects that the gathering started about six months ago in Switzerland. He concludes that something untoward has been going on, but points out that in the nature of things it is going to be very hard to prove it; and even if you could prove it, it would be very hard to bring it home to your suspect. What you really need as firm evidence is the missing bonds themselves, but you feel that they are very unlikely to turn up now.

Nevertheless, you reckon that you have enough on Liselle Goch to make her worth watching, and you arrange for the police to do this. However, you cannot yet tie her in directly to the bomb, although it is beginning to look as though the motive behind the bomb was to distract the attention of her colleagues in the office, while she removed the bonds. You wish that these small private banks had video cameras, as the big ones do. Mark 22 on the Web. You return to your office. Turn to **170**.

197

You return to London, where the nature of the case requires co-ordination at government level. It needs to be assessed whether you have sufficient information to start criminal proceedings, and whether to go for extradition of the suspects, and so on. All these matters have to be referred to the police lawyers and to the office of the public prosecutor. The fact that the criminal suspects belong to a non-EEC country complicates things still more, and the Foreign Office will have to come into the decision-making process. If you have marked 39 on the Web, turn to **68**; otherwise, turn to **91**.

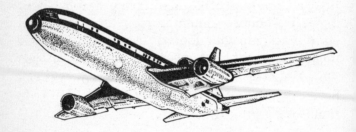

198

You fly to Spain the next morning and land in Barcelona. The local police, whom you had alerted to your arrival and the reason for your visit, have already checked the hotel for you, but the Cohens have left, with no further address known. The hall porter, however, thinks that they hired a car and drove towards Alicante.

It takes a whole day to confirm that they have gone to Alicante and not turned off on the way. The police have a helicopter going down there tomorrow, setting off at lunch-time. Will you go by helicopter (turn to **111**), or will you hire a car and drive there, expecting to arrive not too long after midnight (turn to **246**)?

199

You wait for over an hour; a mist descends and chills you to the bone. Then not just the Lion but a whole crowd of men emerge from the warehouse; there are about twenty of them. They do not look like terrorists at all, but rather dock workers. You reckon that there is some kind of illegal gambling establishment in the warehouse – nothing more than that. You shrink back into your doorway as they pass, but it is inevitable that at least one out of so many will spot you. You are hauled out of the shadows. Will you claim that you were up to nothing untoward (turn to **266**) or not (turn to **280**)?

If you have marked fewer than seven numbers on the Web, you feel that you have not yet completed the preliminary investigations. Turn to **100** to choose another avenue of investigation.

If you have marked more than twelve numbers on the Web, you must turn to **144**.

If you have marked between seven and twelve numbers on the Web, and if any three of the numbers you've marked are *42, 32, 5, 22, 33, 23* or *39*, turn to **250**. If you have marked between seven and twelve numbers on the Web, but fewer than three of the numbers mentioned are among the ones you have marked, turn to **144**.

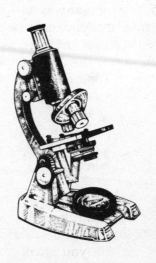

201
Whatever further evidence you have, you do not have enough to wrap up the case. The British authorities are sorry, but after all your hard work they feel they would be compromised if they were to bring criminal proceedings. A good lawyer would tear your incomplete evidence to shreds in court. You must count this investigation as one of your failures. You wonder whether you will ever come across the Spider again . . .

202
Will you now look into the matter of the missing bonds (turn to 164) or of the strange Securicor van (turn to 242), or will you change tack altogether (turn to 200)?

203

You carry on down the mountain, keeping hidden as much as possible, but the walking is easier, and although night is on the way this fits in with your plans. Soon you have a view of the town and you can see lights coming on in houses and on streets. You are directly above the site of the works which you are intending to explore.

You edge closer. You can see that a lot of work is being done: there are piles of rocks, bulldozers chugging around, and many people on the site. One odd thing you notice is that near a cave entrance there is a lot of equipment which looks like air-conditioning ducts, motors and filters. There is also, under a shoulder of the mountainside, what appears to be an underground store, presumably for equipment. You will have to get much closer. You hear the sound of a bell chiming, which you think must be the signal for the end of the day's work. Turn to **232**.

204

You wait for two days. Scotland Yard becomes frustrated at your lack of activity and results. They cancel your contract for this case; you return to London in disgrace.

205

It turns out that you are stranded on what you find to be quite a small island in the middle of a large lake. Distances are deceptive across water, but it seems to you that you are a good five miles from the mainland whichever direction you look in. You consider swimming, but one feel of the icy water deters you: you would freeze to death. You explore the island and find a large box with carrying-handles. It is unlocked. You open it to find a complete set of camping equipment, including de-hydrated stores and even a small heater with a butane gas cylinder.

There are no boats on the island and no signs of habitation. You decide that tomorrow is another day and that you are for the moment too weak to do very much. You erect the tent, make yourself something to eat and drink, lie back in the sleeping-bag, and go to sleep. In the morning you start to think seriously about escaping from the island. A fire might be noticed, but people on the mainland would only think it was a camper. You even toy with the idea of converting the jetty into a raft, but that is even more hopeless. Turn to **31**.

There are only twenty residents involved and twelve of them are embassy or consulate employees and are soon eliminated from your list. The remaining eight whittle down to only one who could fit Cohen's description. You call this man for an interview, but as soon as he walks into the room you realize that he is not your man: he has such a noticeable squint that Cohen would have mentioned it in his description. Will you now look into single males (turn to **93**), those who came with tourist parties (turn to 7), or those who came with family groups (turn to 236)? You may want to check up on the German visitors (turn to 163) or the Austrians (turn to 60). If you have had enough of checking up on visitors, turn to 200.

207

You are certain that Peter Klaus supplied the timer for the bomb and, given his expertise as a mechanic, he is also your prime suspect for the one who assembled it. You cannot place him in London at the time, but maybe he sneaked into the country, or maybe he did not register with British Immigration as visiting London: you checked only the London visitors. You conclude that he is well worth getting to know more about. Turn to 24.

208

It emerges that the bonds were last noticed on the evening before the bomb scare; their absence was discovered later during the day of the bomb scare. Closer interrogation reveals that the place where the bonds were kept was inaccessible before 9.20 a.m., because the safe was secured by a timed lock which opened the safe only at that time. The contents of the safe were constantly changing, and all movements in and out of it should have been noted in a book which was kept by the chief executive of the banking office.

You are forced to the conclusion that the only way in which the bonds could have disappeared was with the active help of one of the four people who had access to the safe during the time that the bonds were unaccounted for. You can start with Tim Mayers, the executive in charge of loans (turn to 25), or Liselle Goch, a Swiss executive on secondment from an Italian bank (turn to 240).

209

Will you go to Harwich yourself (turn to 259), or will you put the matter in the hands of the local Essex police (turn to 102)?

210

The members of the team which you suspect are Thomas Gunn, Richard Penny and Harold Kosinski. The driver, who was spotted, answers to no known description, and was probably taken on to the team only for this job. Your informant told you that Penny was going to take his share of the loot to Bristol, and you know that Kosinski lives in Bristol, so you can search for these two together (turn to 151); alternatively, you can try to track down Gunn (turn to 241).

When you clear the glacier, you find yourself among rocks. The sun has dried them and every crevice in the rocks seems to be full of flowers. You wonder how they survive the cold nights. As the two of you get higher into the mountains, Klaus seems to become happier and his body gets an extra swing into it. You have to remind him that you are not as fit as him and are not as used to the thin air. He apologizes and explains that the mountains were the reason he gave up being an engineer.

Soon you are high enough to see valleys spreading out from the heights and occasional clouds roll by beneath you. It is quite a sight. The roads and towns look tiny; trains look like slow worms rolling along. You climb further and then see something which had been hidden by a ridge – a great scar down the mountainside, as though all life had been gouged out by a chisel. You ask Klaus about it and he looks grim. 'Avalanche,' he says. 'The cause of all our troubles.' Will you press him to say more (turn to **137**) or await another opportunity (turn to **269**)?

212

The report is several pages long, giving extensive facts and figures, but the long and the short of it is that all stores are accounted for, so this is a dead end. If you have not yet looked into the road-building agency, turn to **116**; if you have, turn to **268**.

213

As he pulls up outside his house, your eye is caught by a sudden movement. Instinctively, you push him to one side, and the bullet, which would have hit him in the back, hits his arm instead. You pull him down under the level of the car windows and press the car horn. The would-be assassin disappears. You drive to the hospital, where the doctors take over. He is in pain and bleeding, but he is conscious. As he is wheeled away, he says, 'I owe you my life for that.'

Once you have extricated yourself from the police questioning, for which you have to call in the philosophy tutor to impress them with official identification cards, you return to London. You are now convinced that there is no terrorist connection to the plastic explosive. If you want to get in touch with your contacts in the criminal underworld, turn to **83**. If you want to check up on the manufacturers of the explosive, turn to **261**. If you think you have spent enough time looking into the explosive and you now want to explore another avenue, turn to **200**.

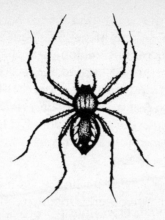

214

While the French police are interviewing him, you listen and watch from behind a fake mirror in the interview room. When the interview comes to an end, you use the internal phone to ask the interviewing officer to find out whether Ulrich was in England at the time of the bomb. Ulrich looks puzzled at the sudden change of direction in the questions, but admits that he was. 'And did he buy a clock in England?' you ask. Now Ulrich looks distinctly worried, and he denies that he bought a clock. But you have witnesses who say that he did. Now he is caught in a bit of trouble: if he is innocent, why should he not buy a clock? It is if he is guilty that he cannot admit it. He denies everything, but he is getting increasingly desperate, and he eventually shuts up and says nothing more.

The police continue to relay your questions to him, but the only further thing he admits to is having been in London at the time of the bomb scare. He says that he was sight-seeing. Through Scotland Yard, who are pleased with your dogged pursuit of Ulrich across Europe, you arrange for the French police to hold Ulrich on suspicion of being involved in the planting of a bomb. The French police are pretty strict, and they assure you that he will not be allowed to communicate with anyone. Mark 5 on the Web. Turn to **200**.

Your occasional brief glimpses, when you risk them, reveal that the two men are walking about, pointing and gesticulating. Their voices echo around the chamber and it is very hard to understand them. It seems to be a technical discussion about the strengths and weaknesses of the building. Dieter explains that the reinforcement has been built like the shell of an egg, and should have the same sort of relative strength. Then the talk moves on to money matters. You hear Klaus say, 'Well, Spinne says that, now that the big matter has been successfully disposed of, we can raise a lot more locally, once people are sure that they will not be presented for payment.' 'No chance,' says Dieter. 'Lisa put almost all of them into the shredder – all but five, which even she couldn't get hold of.' 'Well,' says Klaus, 'five out of a hundred isn't bad: we can pay that out of the rates.' They burst out laughing: the cavern magnifies the noise and makes it seem sinister. If you have marked 35 on the Web, turn to **55**; otherwise, turn to **238**.

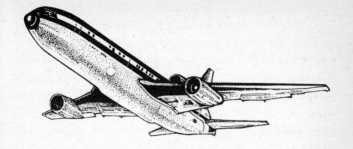

216

You decide to concentrate on the largest amounts first. You find that the £4,750,000 is part of a Swiss loan of £5 million; the £1,500,000 is part of an Italian loan of £5 million; and the sum of £1 million is part of a total loan raised by a Greek shipping company of £4 million.

One thing strikes you as odd. It is usual for banks, when accepting bonds in return for loans, to split them up into a number of smaller quantities, so that if the company or organization which wanted the loan goes bankrupt the losses are spread over quite a few different banks or offices. In this way the loss is minimized, as a sort of insurance: you remember the saying, 'Don't put all your eggs in one basket.' Will you first check up on the Swiss loan (turn to **58**), the Greek loan (turn to **19**) or the Italian loan (turn to **33**)?

217

You ask the hotel for details of Spinne's bill. They show you a copy and you see that the bill was sent to a very respectable German bank. Moreover, it turns out that Spinne seemed to possess no credit cards; in fact, the hotel had felt obliged to make discreet inquiries to the bank about him. They tell you that the bank's reply relieved them of all worry. This is all very curious: a shoemaker, no money of his own, bills sent to a bank which pays them without question. This is definitely worth following up. Turn to **143**.

218

By a lengthy process of elimination, you discover that the relevant lorry is the Swiss one, whose driver, Hans Ulrich, comes from the canton of Untersee, and fits the shop-girl's description. But, by the time you try to locate Ulrich, the trail has gone cold. Mark 23 on the Web and turn to **200**.

219

When you come to, you have a nasty headache. Your heartbeats appear to be banging a drum in your ears and you feel terrible. There is actually the noise of a motor. You gradually realize that you are in the cabin of a small motor boat. You try the door, but it is locked; you shout, but no one comes. The portholes have been boarded up very hurriedly, but you cannot remove the planks. You realize that you must have said or done something that alerted Peter Klaus or his friends.

The water is choppy, but there is no smell of the sea.

When your head clears, you realize that you must be on one of the Swiss lakes. You take further stock of the cabin. When you try to exert pressure on the door, you collapse with the strain. You are still weak from the effect of the drug. Turn to **253**.

220

The villains' launch does eventually arrive in Lisbon – but not before you have had time to wonder often whether you have made a mistake and they were in fact heading elsewhere! However, all it does in Lisbon is refuel, while Thomas Gunn makes a phone call from a public booth on the quay. You hire an inconspicuous but fast launch, in order to continue your pursuit. Meanwhile, you get on to the Portuguese police and arrange that they will provide you with back-up from the landward side and, if the boat looks like going to Spain, alert the Spanish police. Turn to **267**.

221

You feel a slight draught on your face – maybe this tunnel ends in open air! At the same moment, you hear the sound of barking dogs, which greatly increases your chances of being found. You decide that the best thing is to stay put and not risk making any more noises which might give away your position to the people or the dogs. There are so many conflicting scents in the cavern complex that perhaps the dogs will not be much use after all. After what seems like half the night the sounds die away. But has the search been called off? You dare not take the chance. You lie there with the sound of your breathing and the beating of your heart for company.

You stay silent for another thirty minutes, and it is just as well that you do, since the sounds break out again. But this time you hear people saying good night to one another. They must have kept quiet just in case it was a human intruder, who might have given himself away. You wait for another hour, to check that this is not another trick. Then you decide that it is safe to move again. Will you go out of the main entrance, and investigate some of the site huts out there (turn to **44**), or will you move further up the tunnel you are in (turn to **192**)?

Colin Geary is thirty-eight years old and has been a clerk with the company for sixteen years. He is meticulous in his work, but only does what he is told. He has not displayed any great interest in banking in general and does not seem to have the quality of judgement necessary to go further in the profession. Nevertheless, he is very reliable at what he does.

You find that Geary has financial troubles. His salary is not large and he is trying to bring up a family and lead a social life, which costs him more than he can afford. He has loans which cost him quite a bit, but he has nearly finished paying his mortgage and should be clear of his problems in a couple of years.

You can find nothing to connect any of these three employees with the bomb across the road at the Bank of England. Mark *8* on the Web. If you still want to investigate the fourth possible employee, Liselle Goch, turn to 252; if you have already done this, you decide to look into the history of the missing bonds (turn to 265).

223

Wolf Spinne is fast becoming more and more mysterious. You feel you have to base yourself on some kind of reality about him, so you once again get in touch with the Swiss authorities. They confirm that he is just what his passport says – a shoemaker. In fact, he is the town shoemaker in Untersee, and is very well respected. He owns his own house and is married with two children, both of whom now have children of their own. He is just comfortable, as far as money is concerned. If he has been making money, it has not gone either to himself or to his children. Moreover, you find out that if he goes abroad with his wife, as he did last year, he pays for everything himself and they stay in cheap hotels: the German bank with the generous account is not involved at all.

Finally, you are told, in glowing terms, of Spinne's history of public work. He has been a councillor, a town representative and even the Swiss equivalent of mayor for a two-year period. When he was a very young man, he was involved in helping people over the Italian and Austrian borders during the Second

World War: you think this may explain the financial backing of four of the people who fund him. There is also a rumour of his doing similar work during the Hungarian uprising of 1956. Turn to **187**.

224

Having taken Gerald Cohen's statement, you return to London. Will you try to trace the person who told Cohen about the bomb, if only to eliminate him from your possible suspects? If you decide to do this, turn to **128**. Otherwise, turn to **200**.

225

Will you question the townspeople to find out who was responsible for your kidnapping (turn to **41**), seek some other line of investigation locally (turn to **264**), or try to get into the works site where you were refused entry (turn to **243**)?

226

The third part of the file contains a list of political extremists and of those who feel that the Bank is a conspiracy to manipulate world economics. You decide to check up on the politicos, of whom there are ten on the file. They are divided between Marxists who tie themselves into knots and do not really understand their own economic theories, and would-be dictators who feel that they could do the job of controlling the country's economy much better. On reflection, you decide that only one person is worth checking up on. Turn to **65**.

227

You are given the names and locations of the injured terrorist and the agents. If you want to try to extract some information from the terrorist while he is under sedation, turn to **74**. If you want to go and see the agents, to ask if they can help your inquiries, turn to **159**. If you want to bypass British security now, and get in touch with the Soviets, to find out if they have any interest in or knowledge of the bomb, turn to **138**.

228

When the full story is pieced together, as a result of police interrogation, it looks like this: Ulrich brought the plastic explosive, of which Francchi had built up a stock, into the country in his lorry. Klaus brought the timer into the country and assembled the whole bomb. He travelled to London (you have now checked with Immigration – he stayed in Luton) and met with Dieter Francchi. You suspect, but cannot prove, that they also met with the Spider, who would have briefed them about timing. Klaus places the bomb, while Dieter covers him. Klaus then disappears and Dieter tells Cohen to alert the police. Turn to **103**.

229

The constable's report is as follows:

'At 9.19 a.m. a young man, about five foot four inches, with a fresh complexion, slight build, aged about seventeen, and dressed in a pink jacket, pale blue trousers, yellow shirt and blue and white shoes, called excitedly to me, "Officer, Officer, I think somebody has planted a bomb outside the Bank of England." I replied, "Oh, yes." He said in a very agitated manner, "Come and look for yourself, if you don't believe me." I immediately informed my sergeant on my radio that I was proceeding to the scene. I went with the youth to the site and there I found a brown-paper parcel in one of the alcoves where the statues stand. I called my sergeant, who informed me that the Bomb Squad was on its way and that I was to clear the area. While I did so, the youth disappeared into the crowd. My impression was that he was one of the many messengers employed in the City, either by Lloyd's or by the Stock Exchange. He gave his name as John Kaham and said he worked for Gilders. Inquiries at Gilders proved later that they had no one of that name or description working for them.'

Will you start to trace this young man by going to Lloyd's (turn to **49**) or to the Stock Exchange (turn to **36**)?

You have a German friend who is a lawyer and who was very much caught up with the left-wing revolutionary movements. He still maintains a sort of friendship with the lawyers who help to organize and protect the Baader–Meinhoff group of terrorists. Without telling you the names of his sources, he is willing to make inquiries as to whether they were involved, either by providing explosives or more directly in any way. In due course you get his answer. He says that there is no way in which they were involved and asks whether you are sure that the bomb scare was not just a hoax, because it does not seem very serious. Will you next look into a possible Dutch connection (turn to 145) or Arab terrorists (turn to 262)? Or, if you have finished investigating terrorists, will you get in touch with your underground informants, to see if the bomb was the work of British villains (turn to 83), or will you check up on the manufacturers of the explosive (turn to 261)? If you have finished looking into the explosive and want to change tack altogether, turn to 200.

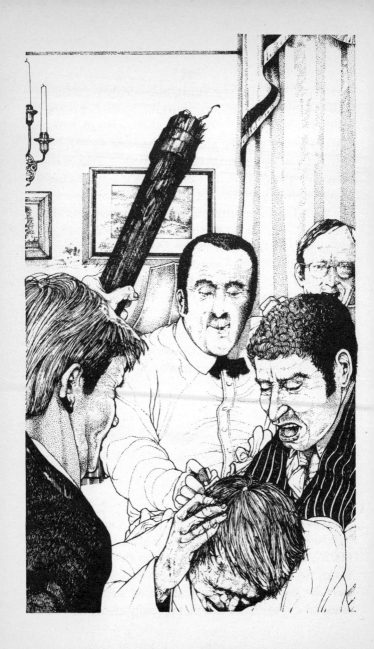

231

The party is rapidly turning into a drunken brawl, with raised voices and people taking offence. One of the arguments is getting loud and very ugly. There is a crash of breaking glass and one man is standing against a wall, waving a broken bottle. You can see that things are getting out of hand; you decide to leave. Before you can get out of the room, however, the man with the broken bottle has been jumped on by two others and disarmed. Then people near you turn on one another with their fists. A chair is broken and you see a man wielding the leg of the chair as a club. It gets perilously close to your head. You dive for the doorway, colliding with two others who have had the same idea. You reach the head of the stairs, but then you feel a stick between your legs. You trip up and fall down the stairs. That's the last you remember. Turn to **88**.

232

You decide to make your move when everybody has gone home. Gradually people leave and then at last you see a man come out carrying a bunch of keys. He locks up some of the huts on the site; the last thing he does is lock up the gate to the road, and then he too leaves. You wait for fifteen more minutes, to make sure the coast is really clear, then you climb down from the crevice where you were hiding, at the base of where the avalanche completed its deadly work. Soon you are inside the locked-up site. Should you risk breaking into one of the huts (turn to 44), or will you make straight for the cave (turn to 94)?

233

You check the ferry and Customs reports and discover that ten possible lorries came into Harwich on the morning that the clock was bought, two days before the bomb scare. Six of the lorries were Dutch, one was Swiss and three were Austrian. If you have marked 10 on the Web, turn to 218; otherwise, turn to 178.

234

The campfire is further than you thought, and it is definitely dark by the time you get to it. You are tired out. There are two men, and you speak to them in Spanish, but 'No comprendo' is all the reply you get. This is obviously a foreigner's attempt to say 'I don't understand' in Spanish, so next you try English – and they are English! You explain about the ranger and they fire off a flare. An hour later, another two rangers appear at the camp, equipped with radios. In the meantime, over cups of hot soup, you have discovered that these Englishmen have met the Cohen brothers and think that they may be in the village, having decided against camping out in the bad weather. You immediately set off for the village. Turn to 276.

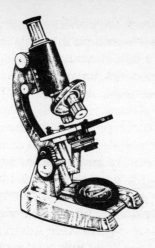

235

The wind blows you past Untersee, and as you look down you can see a large scarred area scooped out of the side of a mountain. You hear Klaus mutter to himself, with venom in his voice, 'Verdammte avalanche.' 'Why do you say so?' you ask. He looks at you with a grim smile and says, 'It is the cause of all our troubles.' 'Why?' you ask. 'Were many killed?' 'Nein,' he replies, 'only two, which is cheap in lives, but the price was heavy.'

'I thought avalanches were only snow,' you say. He laughs out loud. 'Just tons of snow like ice, cutting and gouging through everything; and it starts the rocks moving and the trees and it soon contains small stones and earth, a very good grinding material. The weight too, that squashes buildings and breaks the roofs of caves and causes shifts underground as well – the miners can tell you that.'

But then you both have to concentrate on riding out the wind, which puts paid to any further conversation. After a few hours of glorious, heady flight, you appreciate that you will have to land somewhere for the night. You find yourselves over a high, bleak plateau, somewhere in north Italy, which Klaus says is perfect for landing. You spill the air and the balloon descends. The wind is light now, and it does not take long before you have secured the balloon on the ground. Typically, for Italy, there is a small chapel on the plateau. You are grateful for the prospect of shelter during the night. Turn to **123**.

236
There are only two males involved here and both were with their families at the time. Will you now look into single males (turn to **93**), those who came with tourist parties (turn to **7**), or residents (turn to **206**)? You may still want to check up on the German visitors (turn to **163**) or the Austrians (turn to **60**). If you have had enough of checking up on tourists, turn to **200**.

237
You go to the night club in Soho and get in by mentioning Joe's name. It still costs you £5. You are brought a drink, which costs another £3; you sit down and hope that Joe will not be too long. The club is quite noisy and the atmosphere very rowdy. At last Joe arrives and says – or rather shouts, to make himself heard above the din – that the usual sources of plastic are out of stock, but he could

arrange some if you wanted! You explain that you are not in the market, but are looking for information about the bomb at the Bank of England. Joe looks grave and mutters something about stringing up anyone who tries to damage a British institution; but he tells you that nobody has bought any lately and the underworld knows nothing about the bomb and in fact is quite puzzled about the whole affair.

At the next table, a group of 'Hooray Henrys' are whooping it up a little. You overhear one tell a story about a lady banker whom he knows. She seems, much to the teller's amusement, to have been wandering about the City in cleaner's overalls. The conversation gets louder and someone from another table tells them to shut up; others applaud him. The Hooray Henrys take offence and tell the world in general to mind its own business. Words turn to blows and one young aristocrat receives a punch on his stately jaw. Before you realize it, you are in the middle of a fight. You try to get out of the way, but you are pushed and fall down. You crawl under a table, and at that moment the police arrive. Turn to **167**.

238

Your still-damp clothes take their toll: you sneeze. Peter and Dieter locate the source of the noise easily, and before long you find yourself in the local police station, being charged with trespass and intent to burglarize. You are held there for a few days, which you feel is unnecessarily long – but no doubt it gives the people time to dispose of incriminating evidence, should you try to press charges. When Scotland Yard hears of your nefarious activities, you are taken off the case, before you can cause further international embarrassment.

239

By one of those strokes of luck that occasionally happen in your line of work, Denmark proves very helpful. The wholesalers in Copenhagen are still selling the old design of bag, so they are excluded as a source for the one you are interested in. If you have not already done so, you decide to contact the Swiss wholesalers (turn to 277). If you have now contacted both wholesalers, you ask the forensic laboratories at Scotland Yard if even more refined tests will throw up more information about the bag (turn to 47).

240

Liselle Goch, from the canton of Untersee in Switzerland, is spending time in each department of the private bank, in order to observe the practices and methods of English banking. She has been in London for a few months and has a further six months to spend here. She is well respected, and it is expected that she will be promoted to quite a high post when she returns to her parent bank in Italy, the highly respectable Swiss–Italian bank of Hessemann and Pinelli. No whiff of scandal has ever touched them. If you have not already investigated other employees of the banking office, you may do so by turning to **25**. Otherwise, you could turn to **265** to trace the history of the missing bonds.

241

Thomas Gunn travelled to Manchester on the noon train on the day of the robbery. A plain-clothes policeman remembers seeing him and that he was carrying a small case. If you decide to follow him up to Manchester, turn to **34**. Otherwise, turn to **151** to follow the other two to Bristol.

242

A Securicor van was noted speeding through the traffic in the vicinity of the Bank. In order to achieve this speed, it had to keep changing lanes in a most alarming fashion. Several people noted this and mentioned it later to the police. Its registration number was also noticed.

You feed the registration number into the computer, but the computer demands a security clearance code higher than your own. This implies either that the van was being used by the security forces, or that they know something about it which they want kept under wraps. Do you decide to steer clear of too much involvement in these matters and just to contact one of your acquaintances in MI6 (turn to **176**)? Or do you decide that the matter is important enough for you to pursue it officially with MI6, on the grounds that bomb scares should be of concern to them too (turn to **92**)?

243

You decide not to try to get in the front entrance again, but to climb over the mountain from the other side and approach the site secretly from the rear. You drive round the mountain and hire some camping gear in a small village. The plan that is forming in your mind is to arrive at dusk or after dark, because, even though the site could be innocuous, you do not want to be spotted. The work is supposed to be that of repairing avalanche damage and constructing nuclear fall-out shelters, but you are sure that something else is going on there. Turn to **194**.

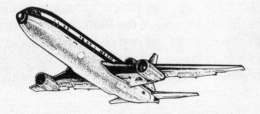

244

The three Austrian lorries travelled to Leeds and were delivering an order of steel to a customer there. Checks with the Leeds firm show that all three lorries arrived at the expected time, the drivers booked into overnight accommodation together, and they even went out to the pub together. All three supervised the unloading and all left together. There is no chance that any or all of them could be involved. Will you now investigate the Dutch lorries (turn to **165**) or the Swiss lorry (turn to **131**)?

245

You fly to Hamburg and on the plane you review
what you know about the Lion. As the name implies, he is a show-off, but also can be very dangerous and unpredictable. You could end up on a
mortuary slab. Since terrorists usually do not oper-
ate in their home base, but use it as a resting-place,
the security services can only watch and report on
comings and goings. The undercover man of the
German security police takes you to the restaurant
where the Lion usually hangs out. You sit down for
a meal, during which you watch the Lion's table,
where he is sitting and holding court. At one point
someone comes into the restaurant, speaks to the
Lion and then immediately leaves. One of the
waiters, who is in the pay of the German undercover agent, slips you a note disguised as a bill,
saying that the visitor spoke in Swiss German. You
know how efficient the German security police are,
and you are sure that the man will have been
followed when he left the restaurant. Sure enough,
you soon hear that he went to the railway station
and bought a ticket for Zurich. Will you follow him
(turn to **70**) or stay watching the Lion (turn to **108**)?

246

The car is fast and you make good time, until at 10
o'clock at night you stop for petrol and decide to
have a coffee as well, in the town of Castellon de la
Plana. In the restaurant you see an acquaintance of
yours, a Spanish detective working on a case involving terrorists belonging to the Basque independence

organization. You spend half an hour chatting to him about an old adventure you shared. When you return to your car, you find that two of your tyres have been slashed. Fortunately, no one goes to bed early in Spain, since they have a siesta in the afternoon, and you find someone to replace the tyres, but it is 2 a.m. before you leave for Alicante. Will you get a move on, in order to arrive there about breakfast time (turn to **67**), or will you drive at a more leisurely pace, considering that you have had little sleep (turn to **158**)?

247

You consider what you have learnt so far from your trip to Untersee. The whole town is uncooperative. The valley has recently suffered from an avalanche. From Klaus's words, you judge that he would reckon that the greater good of the community would justify breaking what he calls 'man-made' laws – which you are paid to defend. So perhaps the avalanche caused damage to the community and he and his fellow conspirators are trying to rectify matters. Turn to **52**.

248

Mark 37 on the Web. You may have recovered the stolen jewellery and received the reward money and the congratulations of the police, but you are no nearer knowing whether the robbers were the ones who planted the bomb; what is worse, when you try to trace them, the trail has gone completely cold. Will you now investigate the missing bonds (turn to **164**) or the strange behaviour of the Securicor van (turn to **242**)? Or will you change tack entirely (turn to **200**)?

249

You go to the branch of the German bank in London and ask them to explain what is going on. They are very reluctant to do so, and you get the run-around: Mr A passes you to Miss B, who says that you will have to see the manager. But the manager is not available: perhaps you would care to see Mr C? And so on. You can take a hint – they do not want you to see anyone of importance at all.

You decide to break through the barriers and you walk straight into the manager's office: his secretary flaps ineffectually at you. The manager claims that clients need secrecy and says that you have no right to the information. This is true, but you know how to put pressure on him. You go back to your office and ring up one of the directors of the bank. You point out to him that he probably would not like it if the security forces of Britain and Germany thought that the bank was trying to shield someone, especially considering that the target appeared to have been the Bank of England. Perhaps, you suggest, the German bank had a personal interest . . . ? The director says, 'Nasty, nasty! Well, I'll see what can be done at the bank tomorrow.' Turn to **3**.

250

You have come across more than one connection with the canton of Untersee in Switzerland. You have an important decision to make. If you think that you have accumulated enough evidence and suspects to make a trip to Untersee worth while, turn to **132**. However, if you think that you still need to make further preliminary inquiries, turn to **100** to choose another avenue of investigation.

251

You realize that such a man would not break his rule not to commit any crime in England, so he cannot be a suspect in your case. Mark **12** on the Web. If you now want to leave Cambridge, turn to **279**. However, if you think that the Eagle may be able to provide you with some information relevant to your investigation, you stay in Cambridge (turn to **5**).

252

You return to the banking office the next day to interview Ms Goch – only to find that she is not in. Hours pass, and she still does not turn up. Phone calls to her flat are unanswered. Her colleagues are worried – and so, for different reasons, are you. You go back to your office and access the Immigration Department's computer. You discover that Liselle Goch left the country early in the morning for South America. You are pretty sure what will happen next, so it is no great shock to be summoned into Scotland Yard and resoundingly rebuked for letting your inquiries spook her, when it looks as though she is deeply involved in a major crime. However much you protest that it may still be possible to implicate her, and even to wrap up the case, Scotland Yard are implacable. You are taken off the case.

253

More sleep seems irresistible, and you have the excuse of wanting to conserve your energy for whatever may lie ahead. You wake up only when the sound of the engine changes: the boat is slowing down. You find a bottle to use as a club, and you stand beside the cabin door. Nothing happens: no one comes. You settle down again. The boat turns, as you can tell by the angle of the cabin door. Then the engine note slows right down and stops. There is a bump and the boat comes to rest. You can hear nothing except clinks and bangs, of which you can make no sense at all.

After a while you try the door again, and this time it opens! You explore the boat. You try the engine controls, but they are dead, of course. You try to get at the engine, but all the doors are securely locked. You see that you are tied up to a jetty, and that a small companionway is laid across from the boat to the jetty. If you decide to stay on the boat, turn to **63**; if you go on shore, turn to **20**.

254

You will never know whether or not the Bristol lorries were involved in anything untoward, because they are long gone from the country. Inquiries with the Dutch company reveal nothing. Will you now investigate some other lorries (turn to **178**), or change tack altogether (turn to **200**)?

255

You find that the actual threats received were just so much hot air – things like, 'If you do not change your money policy, I will mobilize the whole work-force of the British Isles to boycott sterling.' There are a few others, but obviously all from cranks. The Bank has an accessible file of threatening letters and transcripts of phone calls, so it does not take too long to eliminate this thread. Mark 44 on the Web. If you want to explore the idea that the motive was gain, turn to 121; if you think it was revenge, turn to 42.

256

You wonder why the caves are being reinforced with local stone. If this is a nuclear shelter, concrete would make better sense. But if it is a cheese-processing plant, then local stone could be appropriate, as concrete might affect the bacteria which make cheese into cheese with large holes in it. You shut off your torch to see if you know where you are in the dark. It does not seem very successful, so you switch it back on. As you do so, you notice a side passage which you had not seen on the way into the chamber. You can enter this side passage (turn to 278), or you can retrace your steps and take the branch of the main tunnel which you ignored earlier (turn to 135).

257

When you eventually get back to Funchal, you find that the three men you are after hired a launch and have left for an unknown destination. Do you think it is worth trying to follow them (turn to **191**), or will you return to London (turn to **202**)?

258

If the bonds have gone astray, either they must be misfiled in the vault, or they have fallen behind some item of furniture, or they may have been picked up by accident and included in some other parcel of securities. All of these explanations seem most unlikely, but you feel you must cover this avenue. A rigorous search and an auditor's examination do not produce anything except the conviction that, strange though it may seem, the bonds have been stolen. Mark *41* on the Web and turn to **208**.

259

You drive to Harwich. You talk to the manageress of the branch concerned and she checks her lists to confirm that two clocks of that design have been sold since they went on display. She consults her duty rota and tells you which cashiers are most likely to have collected the money for the clocks. However, she feels that it is highly unlikely that a cashier would remember a customer. You decide to talk to the shelf-fillers and assistants first, but they do not remember anything that stands out. You are leaving them to go to interview the cashiers when you notice a slight frown on the face of one of the shelf-fillers. You watch her for a moment or two, and then go up to the manageress and ask if you can take the girl to lunch, since you know that in a more casual atmosphere people often say things which they do not consider important, but which can sometimes be crucial to an investigation. You go to a pub and have a pub lunch, while you talk about this and that. Turn to **272**.

You are surprised by the number of butterflies, insects and birds you see and hear. You find your surroundings very interesting and even idyllic. But it is a very long trek and soon the sun is beating down on you, making you hot, sweaty and thirsty. Fortunately, thirst is soon dealt with, since there are little streams everywhere, which are fed by the melting snow on the high peaks. The water is so cold that it makes your teeth ache. Soon you are coming to the limit of the grassy area; there is still snow on the ground here, and the vegetation begins to thin and appear only in clumps where the snow has melted. The climbing gets quite difficult.

Underfoot, the snow is hard on top, where the snow has melted the top layer and it has refrozen, but soft underneath. This makes walking very tiring, but the sooner you are over the summit the better, so you press on. Then you move on to ice, and you are glad you brought clip-on spikes for your boots. Next even the ice ends and you are making your way over bare rock, cluttered with boulders and patches of loose scree. Although the sun is hot, the wind is extremely cold, but you are well protected with warm clothing.

When you get to the summit, you are able to look down on the town of Untersee. You can clearly see the devastation caused by the avalanche: it looks as though a carpenter's plane has shaved the mountain clean. Nothing is growing where it passed. By now it is getting later than you had hoped. Will you set up camp (turn to **72**) or carry on in the twilight (turn to **8**)?

You start with the British factory in Yorkshire, since it is closest, and find that their records are held on computer disc. They agree to download their complete file on to your computer. It turns out that all the stock this factory supplied to their customers is accounted for; you also discover that the formula for the explosive has been changed in the last year, so you know that your explosive is not old stock, and you do not have to check too far back in the factory's records. You accept, for the time being, that Britain is an unlikely source. Will you now make inquiries at the Austrian factory (turn to **105**) or the French one (turn to **9**)?

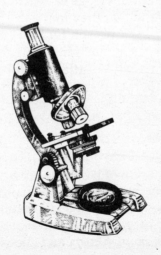

Your main contacts with Arab sources are by telephone, but there are some who can be talked to over the computer network notice-board. You use both methods and eventually learn that the only possibly active groups at the moment are those headed by the Vulture, the Eagle and the Lion. Will you check up on the Vulture (turn to **130**), the Eagle (turn to **22**) or the Lion (turn to **37**)?

Both tourists arrived at the same time, although they did not acknowledge each other in public. The timing suggests that they may have arrived on the train from Frankfurt. You find that seats had been reserved on this train for both of them, but in different carriages. A little more checking reveals that they had both come by train to Frankfurt the day before from Basle in Switzerland. Your suspicions are well and truly aroused – and that is even before you discover that both Peter and Dieter come from Untersee in Switzerland, though Peter now lives in Basle. There is one question in your mind: why did they stop in Frankfurt? Mark **33** on the Web. It looks as though you have found one or two firm suspects here. If you want to investigate Swiss visitors further, turn to **73** and choose again. Or, if you haven't already done so, you may want to check up on the German (turn to **163**) or Austrian (turn to **60**) tourists as well. Otherwise, turn to **200**.

264

You lie low for a few days, even taking the precaution of travelling to another town to ring Scotland Yard: you feel you ought to let them know that, although you may seem inactive, you are on to something big. You do not want them getting impatient and taking you off the case now, when you feel you are so close to solving the matter.

You decide to delve a bit into the past of the town, so you go to the library to look up back-copies of the local paper. An article in an issue from about eighteen months ago catches your eye:

> The results of the winter's avalanche damage are just beginning to show. The summer has uncovered structural damage that the winter snows had hidden. There was even damage to the rock formations of the caves. This was due to the sheer weight of the rock which fell on the roof of the caves. Much work of a structural nature has been started, but there is a great deal more to do. The valley and its co-operative are going to pass through difficult financial times. Herr Engineer Dieter Francchi, who is in charge of the repair work, informs us that it will take another eighteen months to complete the repair work.

You flick through further issues of the newspaper. Turn to **129**.

265

It would be a good idea to check what bonds the missing parcel contained, so you ask for a complete listing. It lists the missing bonds as follows:

95 × £50,000	4,750,000
7 × £20,000	140,000
6 × £100,000	600,000
20 × £75,000	1,500,000
8 × £125,000	1,000,000
1 × £10,000	10,000
£8,000,000	TOTAL

So a total of £8 million pounds' worth of bonds is missing, but you really need information on who borrowed the sums originally. You ask the bank. Turn to **216**.

266

You are roughly asked what you are doing. It is gloomy and you hope that the Lion will not recognize you from the restaurant. But when you start to protest your innocence of anything and everything, this is so implausible in such surroundings that he pulls you under a dockside lamp – and recognizes you. You are rather badly and brutally battered. At the beginning of your second week in hospital, Scotland Yard send a telegram, which reads, 'Sorry, T.S. Time presses. Services terminated.'

267

The boat puts out to sea and then takes a northerly course. You follow at a discreet distance. After some time, you arrive at the mouth of the River Douro, at the port of Oporto, where all the famous brands of port are stored. The villains' boat anchors and again Thomas Gunn goes on shore. After an hour he returns and the boat sets off north again.

Its destination turns out to be Corunna in Spain, where it anchors off shore and makes a signal. Spanish Customs officers come out to the boat, and later return. Meanwhile, you have been on the radio and found out that the Spanish police have been alerted and have been tracking the crooks along the coast. Two fishing vessels come close and start putting out lobster pots; then a fast cruiser sets out from the shore towards you all. Turn to **21**.

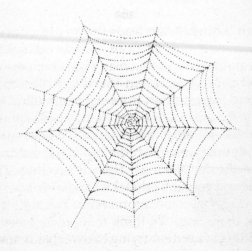

268

At least one thing is clear from the Italian report – that it would be a good idea for you to maintain connections with its author, who has access to a lot of privileged information. You ask him if he has heard any rumours on the political grapevine about the London bomb. He has not, and his opinion is that it was a well-planned amateur effort. This is what you are beginning to think as well. However, you still need to trace the explosive. Mark 45 on the Web. If you have not yet looked into the Austrian factory and wish to do so, turn to **105**. You might still want to explore the possibility that the explosive was supplied by either terrorists (turn to **113**) or criminals (turn to **83**). Alternatively, if you have finished investigating the explosive, turn to **200**.

269

When it is dusk, Klaus leads the way to a hut on the mountains, where you can spend the night. The Swiss mountains contain many such huts as a safety measure, because, when the clouds descend and the wind blows, death from exposure follows fairly swiftly. You arrive and it is indeed a pleasure to sit down to a hot meal, which is soon ready. After the meal, you sit down together with a hot drink and discuss the day's doings. There is a feeling of camaraderie and you think that this is a good opportunity to try to extract some information. You start the ball rolling by saying, 'To think that only a week ago I was sitting at my desk trying to cover blank sheets of paper. It was raining and all I could see was damp brickwork. Have you been on holiday recently, or have you always been working?'

He is not suspicious. He replies that he is always working, but has been away on a special job. 'Oh?' you ask idly. 'Can you talk about it?' He does not answer and starts talking instead about military service. As you know, all Swiss males between sixteen and sixty do armed service for periods from one to ten weeks every year. You ask why, and say, 'Surely Switzerland is neutral?' He laughs. 'That is why we can afford to be neutral. The price of freedom is vigilance and readiness. We need to make it so difficult that it is not worth invading us. Why do you think Hitler left us alone? Remember, we are surrounded by countries who have tried to conquer us many times and we have thrown them all out in the end.' Turn to **35**.

270

The full report on Schmidt gives a breakdown of his income and expenditure (the Swiss police are *very* thorough), his hobbies and his family connections. You do not feel that there is anything suspicious about him at all. If you want to read the report about Popper, turn to **90**; if you want to read the report about Klaus, turn to **186**. If you have finished reading the report about all three, mark 32 on the Web and turn to **200**.

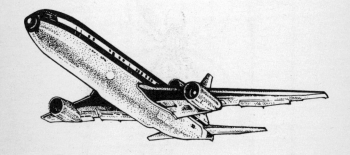

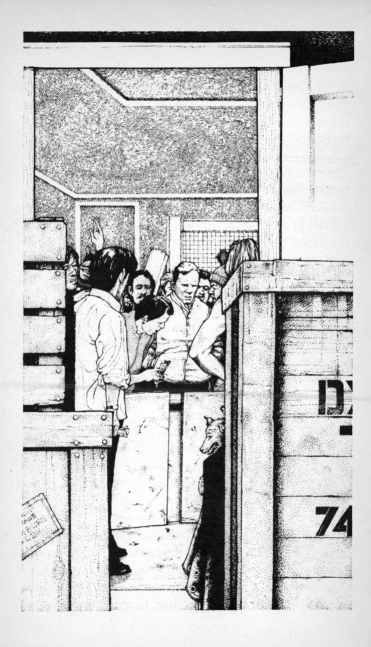

271

You can see very little inside the gloomy warehouse except row upon row of large stacked crates. However, a light is showing under a door across the warehouse floor, and when you approach this door you can hear the confused babble of many shouting voices. The door starts to open and you duck between two rows of crates. A man comes out and makes his way to a far corner of the warehouse, where he goes into a toilet. He has left the door to the noisy room open and you can now see what is going on. This is no meeting of terrorists, but a dog-fight. Two starved animals are being provoked by a score of yelling men into mauling each other to death. The fight has only just started, and money is still changing hands. Then the man returns and closes the door. You leave. You decide that the German agent was right when he told you that the Lion is lying low at the moment: this is probably the height of his nefarious activities – though you shudder to think what plans may be lurking in that devious mind. Mark 58 on the Web. You may now return to London and investigate the Eagle (turn to 22), the Vulture (turn to 130), Dutch terrorist groups (turn to 145) or the Baader–Meinhoff gang (turn to 230). If you have finished exploring the possibility that there is some terrorist connection to the bomb at the Bank of England, you can get in touch with your criminal underworld informants (turn to 83) or the manufacturers of the explosive (turn to 261). If you have finished looking into the explosive and want to change tack altogether, turn to 200.

272

The topic of long-distance lorries enters the conversation as you are talking about the advantages and disadvantages of living in Harwich, which is a port of entry for cross-channel freight. Suddenly the girl's face lights up. 'Now I remember,' she says. 'I wasn't sure which customer it was, but when you asked us I thought, "That's a long-distance lorry-driver, that is", but I couldn't see why I thought that. Then I remembered that that day I'd been doing the shelves and I saw a little roly-poly man go walking around among the clocks and kitchen ware. Well, I didn't give it a lot of thought. I mean, people are always wandering around Woollies; some of them don't buy anything, anyway. After a moment I see that a clock's gone, but so what? But he tripped on the way out and I saw the bottom of his shoe, all shiny it was, as though he'd been polishing it. So I thought, "Lorry-driver", see?' Turn to **233**.

273

This was the result of a rough-house which had followed the detection by some terrorists of a watcher. They had crept up behind him and hit him on the head, none too gently. His department knew where he was, however, and took steps to recover him. MI6 alerted Special Branch, because this terrorist group had Irish connections. Special Branch undertook the job of rescuing the agent before his captors damaged him too much. The terrorist group called themselves the National Revolutionary Liberation Army, and were renowned for their rather stupid brutality.

An ambush was set up. It was to be triggered by an obvious police car pulling up at the premises occupied by the NRLA. The terrorists were alert and moved the agent out of the premises within two minutes in a van. The van was then ambushed at the end of the street. Unfortunately, the encounter was quite violent and two terrorists had lost their lives, while another had been injured and a Special Branch agent had been hurt, as well as the MI6 man they were rescuing.

If you have marked more than three numbers on the Web, turn to **195**. If you have marked three or fewer numbers on the Web, turn to **227**.

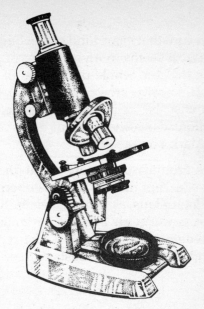

274

You hire a light aircraft with a good cruising range. West leads straight into the Atlantic, so you ask the pilot to make a sweep from the north of the island to the south via the east. Eventually you see a boat which fits the description you were given of the boat the villains hired. They have left Funchal, which is in the south-east of the island, have cleared the south-eastern tip of the island, and have just turned north-east. They could be heading for either Casablanca, in Morocco, or Lisbon, in Portugal. You dare not draw attention to yourself by circling around the boat until you are sure what their destination is, so you have to take a risk. Will you fly on ahead to Casablanca (turn to **12**) or to Lisbon (turn to **220**)?

275

You feel sure that some kind of conspiracy is taking place, and it seems to involve a lot of people. It is unlikely that the whole population of Untersee is criminal, so why are they being so obstructive? There must be something affecting the whole population which they do not wish you to see or know. Mark 3 on the Web.

You ask around some more about Dieter, but get nowhere, except that his name is often linked with that of Peter Klaus, as two old friends. Klaus, as you know, is now a guide living in Basle. Since you can get nowhere with the wall of silence in Untersee itself, you decide to go to Basle and see Klaus. Turn to **24**.

276

You reach the village and go to the local café to phone the police. Then you discover that two of the people in the café are none other than Gerald Cohen and his brother! They are most impressed that you are the famous T.S., whom they have read about in newspapers. You waste no further time in taking Gerald's evidence. Turn to **10**.

277

Your Swiss inquiries do not help, since there is no way for the wholesalers to tell where your bag came from, let alone where it went to. If you have not already contacted the Danish wholesalers, you decide to do so, for the sake of thoroughness (turn to **239**). If you have now contacted both wholesalers, you ask Scotland Yard if their forensic laboratories might be able to use even more refined tests to throw up some information about the bag (turn to **47**).

278

This passage takes you to a chamber which is even larger than the one you have just left. Work here is very much in progress; there are tunnels into the rock and heaps of rock broken by drilling and blasting. Over the ceiling a sort of steel web is being built. There is a great deal of machinery here, covered by tarpaulins. When you look inside the covers, you see that some of the machines are brand new and some are old. Quite a bit of the machinery, both old and new, has been damaged, presumably by the avalanche. A great deal of money must have been lost.

Some of the machinery is designed for cutting and some for squeezing. You assume that this was where the cheeses were made and the curd shaped and so on. But why are all the tunnels being excavated? You go down one of the tunnels. It is not completely finished, but you can see that it is being fitted with racks, which are being lined with local rock; the stones are fitted together so precisely that it would be hard to get a knife-blade between one stone and another. Turn to **110**.

279
If you now want to check up on the Lion instead, turn to **37**; or, if you want to find out about the Vulture's activities, turn to **130**. If you have not done so already, you could look into the possible involvement of terrorists from Holland (turn to **145**) or Germany (turn to **230**). If you have finished investigating terrorists, will you get in touch with your criminal underworld informants (turn to **83**) or check up on the manufacturers of the explosive (turn to **261**)? If you have finished looking into the explosive and want to change tack altogether, turn to **200**.

It is gloomy and you hope that the Lion will not recognize you from the restaurant. You summon up as much Hamburg dockland slang as you can remember and sprinkle your speech with it as you explain that you were looking for a target whose pockets you could pick. They laugh and push you roughly back into the doorway. You suffer nothing worse than a bruised skull. Mark *58* on the Web. You now think that the German agent was right when he told you that the Lion is lying low at the moment, as far as terrorist activities are concerned. You return to London and may now investigate the Eagle (turn to **22**), the Vulture (turn to **130**), Dutch terrorist groups (turn to **145**) or the Baader–Meinhoff gang (turn to **230**). If you have finished exploring the possibility that there is some terrorist connection to the bomb at the Bank of England, you can get in touch with your criminal underworld informants (turn to **83**) or the manufacturers of the explosive (turn to **261**). If you have finished looking into the explosive and want to change tack altogether, turn to **200**.